Southword 38

Southword is published
by Southword Editions
an imprint of the
Munster Literature Centre
Frank O'Connor House
84 Douglas Street
Cork City T12 X802
Ireland

www.munsterlit.ie

 @MunLitCentre

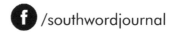 /southwordjournal

#Southword

Issue 38
ISBN 978-1-905002-69-6

Editor
Patrick Cotter

Seán O'Faoláin International Short Story Competition Judge
Billy O'Callaghan

Gregory O'Donoghue International Poetry Competition Judge
Kim Addonizio

Production
James O'Leary

Thank you to Anne Kennedy for her technical assistance

The opinions expressed by contributing writers are not necessarily representative of the publisher's or editors' opinions

© 2020 by the Munster Literature Centre and individual contributors

Cover image: *The ornithologists* from *Paradisi Regained* by *Daphne Rocou*

The Munster Literature Centre is a grateful recipient of funding from

Comhairle Cathrach Chorcaí
Cork City Council

CONTENTS

Please Subscribe

By subscribing, you will receive new issues of *Southword* straight from the printers, as quickly as we will ourselves. Your subscription will also help to provide us with the resources to make *Southword* even better.

Rates for two issues per year:

Ireland, UK, USA	€20 *postage free*
Germany, France, Italy, Spain	€24 *postage free, tax-inclusive*
Rest of the world	€30 *postage included*

For subscriptions and renewals visit www.munsterlit.ie – payment accepted by PayPal.

Southword may also be purchased issue-by-issue through Amazon outlets worldwide and select book shops in Ireland, the UK, Europe and the USA. We keep an up-to-date list of supporting book shops on the www.munsterlit.ie subscriptions page.

THE MUDDY RUDDER
Anthony Walton

I

I began to see (and understand) Seamus Heaney as a person, to stop framing him through the lens of Nobel-recipient and as the all-time literary great "Famous Seamus," on a fall afternoon in the mid-1990s not long after he had been to Stockholm. We'd been acquainted for almost twenty years, and as he had driven through southern Maine on his way to my town of Brunswick, headed farther east, he had noticed the sign of a restaurant, The Muddy Rudder, which sits hard by Interstate Highway 295 in Yarmouth, a small bedroom community fifteen miles north of Portland. Apparently, this sighting had struck him quite powerfully because that afternoon as we talked over coffee and then took a short walk he kept saying to himself, over and over, "The Muddy Rudder."

Over and over again: "The Muddy Rudder." He would play with it rhythmically, rushing and saying it as quickly as he could: "Mud-dy Rud-der," then very slowly and dragged out. "The Muhhhdddd-eeeeeee Ruuhhhhhhd-errrrrrr." He'd alter it phonetically, "The Mah-duh Rah-duh," or metrically, in iambs, "Muh-DY, Ruh-DER," then switch to trochees, "MUHD-dy RUHD-der." This went on all afternoon. It was quite pleasurable to hear, as he spoke with the "energetic, angular, hard-edged"—in his words—intonation of the baritone of his Irish Ulster voice. But it was also instructive, as I began to recognize that the poet I had so long admired, the author of such phonetically melodic masterpieces as "Death of a Naturalist," "Blackberry Picking," and "Two Lorries," was in fact "just" a fellow who loved words, their malleability and almost harmonic possibility. He had written years earlier in "Feeling Into Words" about how much he loved "the bumpy alliterating music, the reporting sounds and ricocheting consonants" he had found engrossing and life-altering in the lyrics of Gerard Manley Hopkins—and there they were. I had a front row seat. That moment taught me that beyond being a *poet*—*the* poet—he was also just another of the many people I knew who love our language, the play, its sound and noise, its endless variation. (And this simple lesson in our common humanity would be brought home again to me by the unforced linguistic playfulness of my daughter who, as a toddler learning to speak, took enormous pleasure in saying certain words such as "Chicago" and "Buffalo" over and over, beautiful words she had discovered in her travels, her reconnaissance of the world and its names.)

Listening to Heaney that day brought the essay "Feeling Into Words" alive, made it real before my eyes. In the essay he speaks of his linguistic bedrock, what he called "the unconscious bedding": "my mother used to recite lists of affixes and suffixes, and Latin roots, with their English meanings… the exotic listing on the wireless dial: Stuttgart, Leipzig, Oslo, Hilversum… the beautiful sprung rhythms"—yet another reference to Hopkins—"of the old BBC weather forecast: Dogger, Rockall, Malin, Shetland, Faroes, Finisterre… the gorgeous and inane phraseology of the catechism." It was how he learned "the bumpy alliterating music, the reporting sounds and ricocheting consonants" of the language he grew up with. And Heaney's infatuation with The Muddy Rudder animated this aspect of his persona; it helped me see and bond with him in a fashion I could not previously have imagined.

All that said, Professor Heaney's enchantment with those simple words has grown in my mind over time, because they have come to represent to me something beyond mere sound (crucially important as that is to verse in general and his in particular). It was as if he lived not with, not among, but *inside* words. As if that mind of his, so widely ranging and notoriously referential and allusive, in fact found words more compelling, more real, more *true*, than the material reality they referred to. And listening to his unconscious adaptive alterations I couldn't help wondering if that phrase "muddy rudder" was somehow working its way toward becoming one of those "symbols adequate to our predicament" that he so forcefully challenged poets to reach for. And what might that mean?

2

I first encountered Seamus Heaney on the page, in John Matthias's Poetry 305 in the English Department at the University of Notre Dame. The year would have been, to the best of my recollection, 1979. I was a sophomore, and beginning to consider poetry something, if it is not too grand a statement, to which I might dedicate my life. We were assigned to read his first omnibus collection, *Poems 1965-1975*, which I enjoyed but would not completely apprehend for years, and, his first book of essays, *Preoccupations*, where I lit upon the magisterial "Feeling Into Words," which had originated as a lecture for the Royal Society of Literature. Not only did it read as if he were sitting across the table gently leading a warm discussion, but it also imparted lesson after lesson after lesson of deep poetic insight, lessons a nineteen-year-old could not have thought he needed, and as that nineteen-year-old grew older and learned a little about poetry and prose, had not realized were possible to convey. Heaney wrote about his immersion in language, poets he had been inspired by, how he had learned to see and think about language as more than mere words. And he explained how a few poems had come about, among them the masterpieces "Undine," "Tollund Man," and "Bogland," and he linked his practice to the English tradition while also laying clues to other languages, like Gaelic and Latin and Danish, and academic disciplines, such as anthropology and archaeology that fed his poetic vision.

I was able to meet and talk with him either that year or the year after and to begin a casual but warm acquaintance that would continue for decades. I remember being startled at his friendliness, and how he would kindly tolerate what seemed even to me at the time as "sophomoric" questions. He visited Notre Dame again before I graduated, and as the years passed I would run into him from time to time at formal readings or at poetry festivals or in bookstores, each time greeted with simplicity and fellow feeling. I remember one day remarking just how much I liked his very brief poem "The Poplar," from *The Spirit Level*, and to this day am warmed by my memory of his sly grin and wink (that was almost a smirk) as he said, "Oh, I like to give myself about one of those a year." And I went back and started counting them up, "Oracle," "Nerthus," "Good-night," "Widgeon," "1.1.87," "Song," "The Strand," and so many more, poems that on first glance appear quiet and negligible but which, with study, erupt with a power outsized to their space on the page.

3

Such memories may seem commonplace, but the circumstance of conversation with and acknowledgement from someone like Seamus was quite important to me, a young person from deep in the provinces. His matter-of-factness gave me confidence, and the ability to meet and talk with other poets and writers, including my great friend and mentor Michael S. Harper, whom I would and would not be surprised to later find out was a dear, long-time friend of Heaney's (Heaney would later come to Maine to introduce and praise Harper at a festival held in Harper's honor at Bowdoin). But as a very young person in 1981, I had had the nerve to approach Harper cold and tell him that I wanted to attend Brown and study with him because the great (I mean that sincerely) Seamus Heaney had taken the time talk to me kindly as a fellow poet.

I was lucky to spend time with him out of the glare of his celebrity. Thinking about it in retrospect, I can see that we might have been more similar than dissimilar, and I have wondered if he somehow intuited that and found me, as such, a congenial companion. We were both the children of farmers (though my family, sharecroppers, had been forced off the land with the advent of the mechanized cotton harvester and like millions of other African Americans had migrated from Mississippi to Chicago, Illinois, where they began new lives and experiences in the industrialized north). Also, Heaney and I had become college-educated, leaping away from those who raised us and into the literary and academic worlds in one fell swoop. And we moved away from, with stealth and perhaps slyness, the staunch, and well-inhabited religious belief and practice of our elders.

I want to be clear, again, that I am seeing these parallels only in retrospect. I wonder if it is possible that there was a perceptible affinity between us, an underlying farmer's unprepossessing manner and even shyness, perhaps, that reminded me of my father and uncles and attracted me to him. And that he also recognized a similar plainspoken reticence in me that signaled along the same frequency. We were both outsiders, "rough customers," who hid it (yes, for all of his sweetness and gentle bonhomie, he was also a strong man, and a tough man), who went away from our religious forebears after being educated in the Church, and who were able to find purchase in both academia and publishing. And perhaps most truly, we were both "split," full of secret thoughts and opinions that we understood were best kept to ourselves, out of both love and respect for those who raised us, those who, though we had less and less in common with them, we still understood were responsible, in act and intention, for everything we were able to accomplish in life even as it sent us away from them. I once heard someone praise Seamus as "a man who had no sides." And I agreed with that for many years, but as I have aged I have begun to think that in fact the opposite was probably true, or more true, that he was more likely a man of many sides, of immense complexity and contradiction, who had devised a public persona that was an aspect of himself, but only one aspect, and which protected the rest of him from the unending demands and pressures of being Seamus Heaney.

We had both been outsiders, orbiting the edges of family, school, community, and tradition since childhood. Seamus Deane told me a story of their childhood at St. Columb's College, a preparatory school in Derry, Northern Ireland, where Heaney had been sent from the farm in Bellaghy to begin his formal education. According to Deane, Heaney didn't join the other boys in their usual games; for example, while most of the students eagerly played soccer, and often took it more seriously than their studies, Heaney would walk in circles around the field memorizing and reciting poetry. And Heaney would talk sometimes to me about the importance of keeping one's own counsel because of the complicatedness of the world(s) he found himself in as a young man. I think he understood or had a sense of what it was like, what it meant, to be an African American, to chronically counter opposition. He spoke to me very plainly about the importance of writing truthfully about the world as one saw it, but also *only* writing, in the end, for the audience of one's self.

Finally, I think he enjoyed talking shop with an occasional friend, who shared his parish of interests. As an African American I was deeply interested in Irish literature, because I thought it showed me a way forward as a writer, quite frankly, for me, a way away from the Black Arts Movement and overtly political practice that was so dominant among black writers in America at the time that I was starting out. I thought about Irish writers who had matured in the crucible of opposition to colonial power in what was, at base, an ethnic war, while having to address these issues in the language of that oppressor.

The situations in Ireland and America were not, of course, exactly analogous, because of the different natures of the conflicts in Ireland and America, the Irish conflict being overt while the American conflict was more subterranean (fought through custom and law with selective terrorism rather than guerrilla war), but Irish writers also had to deal with the violent loss of loved ones, and that showed me ways of writing about those moments with what was, for me, dignity and honor.

An example of this was a poem of mine, "Drive-By," about an innocent cousin shot in the gang wars of Chicago. I was able to see and develop the poem because of the example of Seamus's "Casualty." At the time that I was beginning these studies of Irish poets and writers I thought this African American – Irish link was an original insight, but I was later to learn that older African American writers such as Harlem Renaissance leader James Weldon Johnson had conceived of similar correspondences decades before (including his explicit encouragement of black writers of that era to learn from the writers of the Irish Renaissance). What I could learn from Irish literary practice was and is crucial to me; being able to learn some of these strategies from Seamus Heaney was a bit beyond belief.

When I wrote my first book, *Mississippi*, I kept the example of Heaney and Irish writers front of mind. I wanted to write about my family, history, politics, and culture. I wanted, in the hubris of a first-time author, to do it all at the same time. As I worked, I thought about Seamus, and some of the things he had said to me, including "write for you." I thought about how he had allowed himself to be both gentle and scathing, how he wrote about the love and shelter his family members had provided for each other, while not flinching from the truth about the brutal conflicts they found themselves surrounded by, and how they were made to feel like alienated strangers within the landscape of their birth. I tried to tell the truth about all of it. I also included poems in the book, which was principally a prose narrative, because I found that there were things I could not say in prose, they were beyond my narrative skills at that time. And of course, I had the models that Heaney had been providing for decades.

That book, *Mississippi*, would become something of a public success, and received a Whiting Award, a prize given to younger American writers. The master of ceremonies that day in New York City was Seamus Heaney and while it may, of course, have been a coincidence, I cannot help but wonder if he had something to do with my award. It was as if a circle had closed, twenty years after we had met. Something else had happened earlier on that trip, which provided another window into him as a person: we were in the lobby of the Morgans Hotel on Madison, chatting, when a young woman approached him, alerting him that she had unfortunate news: Ted Hughes had just died. He flinched, staggered, thanked her, and with wet eyes asked if he could be excused.

I had known he was friends with Hughes but had not known how close. It would be moving to learn over the next few years how deep a debt Heaney felt toward a man who, from a distance, seemed tempestuous and controversial. Hughes had been Heaney's earliest champion and support, the literary friend who made things possible with encouragement, introductions, and publications. And I have wondered if the sorts of encouragement Heaney showed me and many others had been born out of the difference that Hughes's help had made in his own life.

4

These days, I look back at how he signed my copies of his books, and think about the messages, which I like to think were intended for me, and to extend over time:

Two examples: he signed *North* with a couplet from the eponymous title poem, pointing to language and violence and history, and how they were entwined:

> Keep your eye clear
> As the bleb of the icicle

And he signed his collected, *Opened Ground*, with a simple command, in large block print: "KEEP DIGGING."

5

This essay is a form of digging, as it brings me back to the most pleasurable, and dear, moment I spent with him, for several hours late one evening in Brunswick, after he had given his "praise-talk" for Michael S. Harper, which served as the opening event of the Harper Festival. The excited energy of his talk had died down, everyone else had dispersed, and he looked at me and said with a wink, "Lad, how about a crawl?" I thought I knew what he meant, and I said, "That sounds lovely, but there's only one pub in Brunswick." He shrugged genially, "We'll make do."

So we walked from the Bowdoin Campus down into the center of town, where we got a table at Joshua's Tap, a bar named in honor of Brunswick resident, Civil War hero, and all around Maine luminary Joshua Lawrence Chamberlain. After a moment or two discussing the greatness of Chamberlain, Seamus tapped the table with both hands and asked, "What are you having?" to which I replied, playfully, "Whatever is proper." He went to the bar and came back with a whiskey and a Guinness, and as I was determining which was for me, he spun, went back to the counter, and returned with another whiskey and another Guinness. I'm not much of a drinker, but I figured I could handle a round, and we drank and talked about family, especially the hovering aunts we had had who had been of such protection and encouragement (I had mentioned his beloved aunt Mary Heaney in my introduction to his talk).

As we finished that first round, I thought that was that, and prepared to walk him to his hotel, down along the Androscoggin River on the far end of town, but he rolled his shoulders, looked at me and said, "Time to stroll." So, we walked back up the hill toward campus, as far as the First Parish Church (known for, among other things, being the place where Harriet Beecher Stowe had the vision that led to the composition of *Uncle Tom's Cabin*), then turned and walked back down to Joshua's where he had another round and I switched to ginger ale.

This happened two more times that evening, until well after closing, us having drinks at Joshua, then "strolling" back up to First Parish Church and back down the hill to the center of town. Our conversation segued into shop talk, and centered on my asking him questions which he answered with the patience and generosity that is the hallmark of my memories of him, or how he behaved toward me, always. As I have gotten older, I have recognized just how kind he was to me, because I asked what many poets and writers would consider annoying questions like, "When you were putting together *North*, did you realize what you had?" To which he answered, after a moment's thought, "No, it hadn't occurred to me. I just thought it was time to put together another book, and then when I assembled things, started pushing things back and forth, it struck me that there might be something there, something I hadn't seen."

Another of my questions that evening had been, "If there is one novelist you think I should study, who is it?" Again, he thought for a moment, then said, simply, "Banville." I looked at him quizzically, trying to prompt further commentary, but all he would say was, "Banville. You'll see." The next day I began systematically studying the oeuvre of John Banville, Seamus's fellow Irish luminary, and was startled to discover the range of the novelist's thought and accomplishment, from novels about Copernicus, Kepler, and Newton to what could only be described as elevated crime novels, and polished English prose that could be deployed in hard-nosed noir or fully imagined magical realism. I was, to put it plainly, flattered that he thought I was up to such accomplishment, but I was also moved that Seamus, an Irishman, saw me as someone who might be interested in the very best work, the most polished, complex, and far-ranging, contemporary literature our language had to offer. He saw *me*, in both my hunger and my accomplishment. Which, I have to say as an African American, doesn't always happen.

In reflection, I am startled, and slightly unbelieving that I had such times with him. It strikes me as one of the most fortunate gifts in a literary career (such as it is) and life that has been full of such good fortune. We are often counseled to, and I think wisely, avoid meeting our heroes, because they are invariably disappointing when encountered in the flesh, but with him, for me, if anything, it was decidedly the opposite. I thought more of him the more I saw him. And I am quite aware that I only saw a small part of him, a portion that he chose to allow or present, but that sliver of the wide-ranging complexity that was Seamus Heaney was a gift of immensity to me, and I am lucky to have received it. And I can hope, and perhaps surmise, because he was so amenable to spending time and sincerely engaging with me, that maybe I provided something to him.

6

Remembering that afternoon of "The Muddy Rudder," I sometimes think of what Heaney wrote about James Joyce in "Station Island":

"His voice eddying with the vowels of all rivers came back to me."

There is that triumvirate again: voice, language, landscape. Landscape—Heaney's playful iterations of "the muddy rudder" made me think of the marsh (and strand) at low tide, and also of that rudder deep in the floor of the mud, dredging roughly, even violently, through the wet soil. And though the marshes of coastal Maine are not exact analogues for the bogs of Ireland and Northern Europe, it is fascinating to think about them in conjunction with Heaney, what he might have been conjuring as he looked out of the car from the highway that afternoon and saw the boggy marshland stretch into the distance: "Looking back to ramification of roots and associations and forward to a clarification of sense and meaning."

Those Maine marshes are tidal, meaning that sometimes there is more water and sometimes less, but when the tide goes out, we are left with what is revealed, an ecology, which, in Heaney's overarching trope, we can study as if it were an archaeological dig: the alluvial soil, vegetation, mollusks living and dead, garbage. And you might start to intuit, as he did, that it contains, in a metaphoric leap, human history, including bodies with stories to tell. Again, his own words: "Almost unnameable energies that, for me, hovered over certain bits of language and landscape."

Seamus was known for his obsession with the boglands, and I have wondered if his obsession that afternoon with "muddy" and "rudder" had something to do with his psychic connection to those mixtures of earth and water that, through poetic exploration, contributed to his creation of one of the most accomplished bodies of work in the 20th and 21st centuries. I think of some of the other names for bogs: wetlands, mire, or my favorite, *quagmire*, with its tough consonants and Heaney-ian multiple entendres. It comes from "quag," an archaic noun meaning a marshy or boggy place (and which is probably descended from words of shaking movement like "quake" and "quick"), and "mire," "a stretch of swampy or boggy ground." "Mire" can also, wonderfully, function as a deeply rich verb, where to "mire" something is to "cause to be stuck in mud." And there we are again, in the mud, of the earth, the landscape, and of language, contemplating, as he said, "words as bearers of history and mystery."

I've also wondered if he was, in his conscious and unconscious repetition, telling me something: that it was possible for an artifact as plain and rudimentary as the name of a restaurant built for tourists in a small town on the Maine coast to work its way toward becoming "a symbol adequate to our predicament." I have thought about what a rudder is, and what it means for one to become muddy. A rudder, of course, guides us through water, gliding as we sail, and if it is muddy then it has been stuck, run aground. And to extract it will require labor and time, patience, wisdom. And that mud will erode away either from our intentional washing or inevitably, with time and travel. Whether Seamus was contemplating all that, or "merely" playing with the sounds, he was teaching me to think about it, to take it seriously, and I, who drive past that sign four or five times a week now have a reminder of the poet's task, and duty. It serves as a regular reminder of the man whose example helped teach me who I am, and how seriously I should take my calling, and how lightly that calling can be worn.

MURIEL SPARK'S LOVE RECOVERY CLUB
Theresa Muñoz

'I was always a bad picker of men' – Muriel Spark

I imagine their hands but not their faces.
Their hands tell a gritty story, fists like bud tulips.
What I called Muriel's love recovery club,
men who penned disturbing notes and clutched them,
jacket full of coins, to the post box.

Sometimes Muriel replied and sometimes she ghosted them.
Why didn't you answer me, they shouted,
coveting her star sign and curvaceous signature.
MISS SPARK, you must HELP ME!!!
Those exclamation marks are like shudders, I scribble
as a carnal sunset stripes the room.

When the men typed on mint-white paper,
they signed in bolded font, a clue to vocal level.
I imagine hand prints; watermarks on book covers.
How some men talk to women is a mystery to me.
Beer droplets on their lip, clouding my seashell ear,
giving compliments that boomerang:

like one man wrote to Muriel: *you project*
your desires with zest and vigour
an internal high five to his own self. I'd seen it before
in a frosted glass, our shoulders like twin violin bows,
but he was only seeing himself, in blue eyed wonder.

A person's love is surprising,
and so is their anger. Triggers in her novels:
barn doors, lace petticoats lifted in attics, leather smells
became mother, wife, loveless house, girls in pastel sweaters
who blanked their jokes. Their hands, I imagine,
rigid as pitchforks, scoring air to express
hate for the women in her books.
What did you want to achieve? one demanded,
You are a disgrace to literature.

If a man hits you, get out. But when a liquid rage
washed over his face, the sudden boat-like motion
made my mouth taste of pennies, then he stormed off first.
For weeks I pined into the abyss
of shop windows, until it was safe to forget.
What an idiot, me. I'd be different now. I wouldn't push it away.
When Muriel declined to reply, she scribbled 'File',
for Penelope, her longtime companion, to look after.

You talk to comfort yourself and that's what they did,
explaining the arc of her novels to her.
How she was different, in a good way.
I should like to shower you with gifts, one said.
It is cold and sunny in New York
I like Memento Mori very much, wrote another.

I don't know what Muriel thought of the letters.
Maybe she lay them down, sun on tweed sofas,
several cats outside in the long grass.
I imagine her hands, fingertips like pencil erasers
tracing words of men who mistreated her,
of all the men, who mistreated her
folded, folding them away.

COME CLOSER
Mike Allen

1st Prize, Seán O'Faoláin International Short Story Competition

She tells me about ancient lines drawn in red ochre on the ceiling of a Spanish cave. Apparently, at first, the lines seem random and abstract—arbitrary markings, simple shapes—but if looked at in a certain way they begin to shift and coalesce, cohering into a single figure: a *babirusa*, or deer-pig. Just think, she says. This could be a record of the moment our species first woke up to its own cognition. The modern mind switched on like a light.

✻

The flat is small but the rent is reduced because of damp. There are blemishes around the plug sockets and light switches the colour of old teeth. Dark patches bloom beneath the windows, the wallpaper collecting more water, more weight, until it begins to peel away.

✻

The corners of the carpet are curling and one edge doesn't quite reach the skirting. I pull up a corner and find an empty envelope, some fragile newspaper dating from the eighties, and a scattering of old copper pennies, hard and bright, buried like arrowheads beneath.

✻

Our life together is filled with other people's things. The mint-green towels are on loan from my aunt. The kettle and bed sheets we borrowed from her older sister. Whoever lived here last left an empty suitcase under the bed. Our fridge door is covered in magnets from places we haven't been.

✧

She has asserted herself everywhere with long black hairs that coil on the balding carpet. Her patterned socks decorate the radiators. Abandoned cups perch at the edge of any available surface. The only things that are mine are a warped Wilko frying pan and a Moka pot with a scorched base that will probably always taste of soap.

✧

The gummy seal around the windows has rotted and crumbles when touched. In the little cupboard with the gas meter, there's a black plastic bucket containing a spirit level, several hardened paint brushes and variously sized screwdrivers—simple tools for forgotten jobs.

✧

I don't trust our sofa, its crusty cavities. I've found all kinds of things between the cushions—forks, crushed cigarettes, a tiny key that doesn't fit anywhere. This morning I found, buried in the gap beneath the armrest, a crystal turtle about the size of my fist. At least I thought it was crystal—Swarovski or something. I showed it to her and she turned it over, looking for a mark. Not Swarovski. Not even crystal, she said after looking it up online, just a cheap glass turtle. She put it on the windowsill by the sprig of mint that will not grow.

✧

Humans can sleep for days at a time if there's no light, she says, using the showerhead to rinse her hair over the side of the tub in nothing but her knickers. Two towels, one large, one small, are heaped on the floor by her feet. I am stood precariously on a folding chair with a burnt-out bulb in my hand. The glass light fitting in the bathroom is oddly baroque, misted and bell-shaped, with a scalloped trim that gives it the look of a deepwater jellyfish. The glass is stained slightly yellow, from heat exposure, I suppose, and a new too-long energy-saving bulb peeps rudely from the opening.

✵

I move what furniture we have to cover the scars in the carpet, careful to step over the dirty plates, empty yoghurt pots, magazines, assorted receipts and crumpled tissues that cluster on the floor around wherever she happens to be. I clean the tiny kitchenette, which is really just a sink, a fridge, an electric hob, and a blue arrangement of lino floor tiles that cut into the corner of the living room. The lino is partially lit by a golden, noirish light from the not-quite-neon of the Chinese takeaway across the road. There is a square of less discoloured tiles where once a washing machine might have stood.

✵

She slumps on the sofa, pulls her legs up and hooks them around a cushion. She opens a magazine and picks the polish off her nails, pries pistachios apart and drops their shells into a chipped Tinkerbell cup which is also an ashtray.

✵

She sits on the floor making lists—spiral-bound notepads and Post-its and the backs of council tax letters—lists filled with hopes, plans, and possibilities, all written in a loose, whirlwind hand.

✵

She has a habit of spilling her entire life onto the bed and leaving it there for me to clear up.

✻

I shake the old bulb and listen to its frazzled filament sing tinnily in my ear. She asks me why I haven't thrown it away. They don't make these bulbs anymore, I say. This bulb marks the end of an era. This bulb is a relic. She has this way of looking at me with a sideways squint as though I've just told a joke.

✻

I find her submerged in milky bathwater. It flows between her glowing knees, around the simple symmetry of her breasts, and collects in the hollow notch at the base of her neck. Soaps, lit candles, teacups, razors, lotions, shampoos and sea salt scrubs are balanced on the shallow ledge surrounding the tub. She closes her eyes and slides under until she is nose-deep, a voice from the laptop guiding her to connect to her breath. I summon the strength to do the washing up, filling the sink with water that takes forever to get warm. On the TV refugees are moving north in their thousands, crossing the Mediterranean at night in crowded boats. They carry children, passports, painkillers, bottled water, torches, plastic bags, sellotape, cigarettes, dates, lemons. They travel unimaginable distances to cross abstract borders. I let a plate drift to the bottom of the sink with a soft clunk, then drain the water and watch the foam flush away. Almost simultaneously I hear the bath emptying and the gutter gurgles outside, connecting us via an endless series of pipes and sewers and tributaries to any possible ocean.

✻

We notice a bad smell coming from somewhere—a fusty, deathly smell—and trace it to a potentially noxious blue-grey mould evolving into something increasingly sinister under the bathroom sink. It's even more pungent up close. I think I feel my throat constrict and spend hours on the laptop researching respiratory symptoms: lung infections, chronic fatigue, assorted autoimmune diseases. I take pictures and email the landlord, whose auto-reply states that he is away for two weeks and isn't picking up his phone. I lie awake at night imagining billions of minuscule airborne spores swarming through the rooms to coat our lungs and infest our blood.

*

I light candles and place them by the glass turtle and old bulb like a prayer. I water the brittle sprig of mint. I scrub blackened stains from the hob with a haggard scourer. There are watermarks beneath the glass that cannot be undone.

*

At seven o'clock she is sat on the sofa watching a documentary about cave paintings. She is clipping her toenails onto a square of kitchen paper, and there are two half cups of tea and an open packet of Hobnobs balanced on the cushion beside her. I think she has forgotten that we are supposed to be going out. I sit on the arm of the sofa and ask her about the caves. She says that they were discovered a hundred years ago somewhere in northern Spain and that they contain the earliest known images made by modern humans or possibly even Neanderthals— animals and abstract symbols and hand impressions in charcoal and red and yellow pigment that have been sitting below ground in the dark for over 65,000 years. Then she looks up at me and says, You're wearing a shirt.

*

We stay up late on the sofa drinking Co-op wine and watching Blue Planet with the lights off, the colours from the screen swimming over the bare walls. We try a thing she's read in a magazine where if you stare into another person's eyes for long enough your heartbeats slowly synchronise. For a minute or more we look at each other in silence, holding hands, trying not to smile. Then, in perfect unison, we both whisper, Is it working?

*

She stands to execute a sun salutation as we're watching Newsnight, her arms stretched towards the ceiling, legs spread, fingers reaching. I can see the twin dimples at the base of her back as her T-shirt lifts, while men on the TV search the rubble for survivors following an earthquake somewhere in the Middle East.

*

I watch her prepare for bed, her face wash routine, the way she tilts her head as she brushes her teeth. Her teeth are small and sweetly crooked. She works up a fluoride spume and spits and taps the brush on the edge of the sink like a conductor.

*

Lying on the bed, with my ear pressed to her chest, I can hear the blood humming through her as she sleeps. The slight dent from a hair band encircles her wrist.

*

She shuffles about in my hoodie and a pair of scuffed Uggs complaining about the cold because she is suffering, she is sick. The radiators gurgle but they're all talk.

The radial control on the boiler is an arcane device governed by a dark art that I do not understand, and the manual, a wrinkled paper booklet, is stuck face-down to the top of the fridge. I put my ear to the radiators and can hear them whispering. When I turn their dials all the way up the pipes let out a collective sigh and something groans beneath the floorboards. Voices! she says, throwing her arms up in the air. I hear voices!

*

We spend an evening pulling whole swathes of wallpaper off in great strips, exposing the yellowish plaster beneath. We discover a complex network of delicate cracks, vast contours of damp spreading in all directions, hidden geographies. There is a telephone number scrawled at shoulder height by the light switch. A constellation of small polyfilled holes makes a rectangular pattern where perhaps a phone was once affixed. We move the sofa and peel more paper away to uncover a series of markings in bright crayon—mostly senseless scribbles, children's doodles, although some look a little like people or animals. I trace the possible outline of a hand or bird-thing with my fingers. I follow two distinct lines that rise separately from the skirting board like legs to meet in a waist-high arc the shape of a wishbone, then sprout at the apex into a sudden storm of swirls, rising bloomingly as smoke rises from a volcano, before departing in a blunt downwards stroke, a crude nudge into female form. Now that, she says, raising her eyebrows over a milky tea, is a vagina.

*

For the risotto, I have replaced the dried porcini mushrooms with soggy white ones and the chestnut mushrooms with extra rice. I pour in half a glass of cheap white wine and am slowly drinking my way through the rest of the bottle. I have lost all sense of the whole. I stare too long at the squiggles on the walls and they begin to writhe. I think of fractals, streams, cauliflowers, capillaries, lungs. I refill my glass and focus instead on the simple pleasure of a pot of boiling peas, waiting for things to take some kind of form.

*

She lowers the folded paperback into her lap, frowns, then raises it again. Moments later she slaps it onto the arm of the sofa, stands up, shakes her head and walks away. This means she thinks it is good. If she is really enjoying something, she makes a sound of utter disgust.

*

I find a hardened lemon down in the sticky space beside the fridge and it feels hollow, almost weightless, like a carbon copy of a lemon.

*

In the darkness I listen. I feel my way to the bed. I slither across the sheets to lie stretched on my side, one arm extended beneath the pillow above my head, my hips slightly twisted. I press my knee gently, snugly into the crook of her leg. I slide my right hand into the fold of her arm, past her ribs, and place it on the soft swell of her belly. I search for the heat of her breath. I kiss her crusty winter lips.

*

She tells me to wake her up when the documentary finishes but I don't wake her. Her hand grows heavy on my chest as she drifts into sleep, the slightest increase in weight as a sponge grows heavy with water. I think of those ancient humans descending into the underworld to make their mark. They went as far as their fires would take them, sometimes so far that they could not find their way out again. What drove them to go so deep?

THE RULES
Peter Hughes

2nd Prize, Seán O'Faoláin International Short Story Competition

---

Gerry McQuaid.

Gerry The Quaid, they called him. He was one of the Big Boys. He'd gather the smaller boys into Cassidy's Shed to give them lectures on sex.

'Rub a woman's diddies too much and they'll get so hard they'll crack open,' he warned us.

'All the milk'd run out then,' Jersey Joe Sloan shouted out one time.

'For fuck sake,' McQuaid said, disgusted.

McQuaid would produce the cards and play Stripjack Naked with the smaller boys.

You'd play until you were down to just your underpants. But you'd never take off the underpants, you'd stop then. That was the rules.

McQuaid's broad, leery face looking at you as you sat there, shivering. He had slanty sort of eyes, and when he grinned he looked like a Chinaman.

'What were you playing with that wee yella bastard for?' I was occasionally asked at home.

They never found Gerry's head, apparently.

The box – the coffin, I should say – they flew home from England for the mother and sister to bury had most of the rest of him: torso, limbs, those yokes. But the head was never got.

A chainsaw, seemingly. He'd been running with the wrong crowd in London, a drugs crowd. Cops had intercepted a big haul, and there were recriminations. Gerry's flat was raided a while before, and he was looking at a stretch. The word got out that he'd mouthed.

Maybe he did. Maybe he didn't. A ew lads called round one evening and set the big green Boss chugging. VA-WROOM-ARRR! The slanty eyes would fairly have widened then.

The wake house was an uncomfortable spot.

You'd think in all the circumstances they'd have just brought the coffin to the chapel. But Mrs McQuaid was insistent.

'He's coming home to 27 and there'll be a wake,' she told them, her own wee head trembling.

Naturally, it was a closed coffin. Coppery pine shining on its stand in the small bedroom. Mrs McQuaid perched beside it on a chair, blinking like a frail raven at the sympathisers.

'They should have had her open,' Breslin said.

'How could they have?' I asked him.

'The Ghoul could have rigged something up.'

The Ghoul was a name they had on Harry Pearse, the undertaker. It wasn't a nice name, but it suited him.

'In what way?'

'Got a dummy head, done her up. Stuck a greasy wig on it, painted on a big cheesy grin. It would have been Gerry to a T.'

'The Ghoul would have had his work cut out,' Finnegan said. 'He'd be sewing more than a dummy head back on that boy. Them heroin fellas know how to deal with a tout.'

We were sitting sipping bottles of stout in the living room. The door to the bungalow's small back bedroom was open. A priest was standing to one side of the coffin, his head bent down to Mrs McQuaid. She was staring straight ahead, a tiny tremor running up and down her.

People came and went to the wake room in drips and drabs.

'You all right, lads? Couple of stouts?'

Josie McQuaid was buzzing around the sitting room, seeing who needed what.

'We're alright,' I said. 'We'll just sip over these, Josie.'

'Were youse in with the mother yet?'

'Not yet,' Breslin told her. 'We'll go in shortly. How is she, pet?'

'Hasn't spoken six words since they took him home. This'll kill her. She'll be the next one for Latlurcan.'

That was where the graveyard was, Latlurcan.

'Give us a shout if youse get dry,' Josie said.

'I tackled her one night,' Finnegan said, when Josie had moved away. 'In the football field.'

'In a match?' I asked him.

'No – down behind the changing rooms. We were at it hot and heavy. One summer's night, years ago. Jesus, she's put on a bit of kit since then.'

'That was some spot for a scrab at a woman, the changing rooms,' Breslin reflected. 'You could get in through the back window. Just lift the latch and climb through.'

'That wee window?' I asked. 'Contortionist, were you?'

'Aw, I was a limber boy in those days,' Breslin said. 'Me and Dixi Lester got in one night. Loaded, the two of us. Had a go at one another in the showers.'

'Getawayathat,' Finnegan said. 'That's from some blue movie you watched.'

'No lie, Finnegan. No lie. It was a disaster, though. No light in the place, and one of them big communal showers. We got them on somehow, stripped off and in. Ice cold, man. Dixi screeched like a banshee and raced out. Me balls shrivelled to raisins when the water hit them. Couldn't find the clothes, then. Didn't know what belonged to who when we did. Her yelping and cursing and soaking. Got most of the clothes on us eventually and got out. She was a whingeing bitch, that Dixi Lester. Always remember the feel of her wet bare behind under her skirt as I pushed her out the window. Disaster.'

'What was Josie like?' I asked Finnegan.

His voice changed. '"Take your time." I remember her telling me that, take me time. Big warm arms. Moonlight and her shushing me. "Take your time." God, she's put on some kit, that girl.'

Josie was walking from the hall into the sitting room. She was flushed, and smiling.

'Come on ahead, Joe,' she called back over her shoulder. 'You're so good, coming all that way. You'll have to see Ma.'

This small, hesitant man followed Josie into the room. The face didn't click with me, but Breslin got him immediately.

'Holy Christ, that's Jersey Joe.'

You could see it then, in the straw colour of the untidy wisps of hair, and the crouched, apologetic way he ambled along after Josie – the same Jersey Joe Sloan that knocked around Cassidy's Shed and played over the fields with us when we were small.

'Where did he come out of?' Finnegan wondered.

'Lying around London, last I heard,' Breslin said.

Joe wore a battered green combat jacket and he had a canvas travelling bag slung over his shoulder, like he'd just arrived back from hitchhiking around the world.

'Has he still the gansie on him, I wonder?' said Finnegan.

Joe wasn't Jersey Joe because of the old boxer. As a kid, he wore the same blue jersey day after day after day. It was comical – well, we thought so at the time.

'This is our chance,' Breslin said. 'Follow Joe in, do the handshaking bit, then collar Joe and bate it down the street for a few pints of auld lang syne. He's our ticket out of here.'

Breslin tipped Joe on the shoulder at the door, winked when he turned around. 'Aw God, the boys – good to see youse,' Joe said. We all shook hands.

He was rough up close. He smelled stale and his pouchy eyes were too lively.

We took the free chairs by the wall while Josie took Joe over to the mother.

Joe was talking to Mrs McQuaid for a while before heads started to turn.

There was an orchestra of low chat in the room, and all the other instruments, one by one, stopped playing, letting Joe's drawling voice, still like a wee boy's but with a cigarette brattle mixed in, come to the front.

Mrs McQuaid seemed to be repeating the odd thing Joe was saying, nodding a bit more deliberately than usual, not looking at him.

'Good fun youse all had together, Joe, I know. Good fun.'

'Aye, good fun. Real good fun. Good fun.' Joe shook his own head a bit.

'Like the cards, boys, eh, remember them?' Joe jerked his head round to us. His voice was louder now. He had the room's undivided attention.

When none of us answered him, he went on.

'Aye, the cards, the Stripjack Naked at the back of the shed. We all used to play it and down to your underpants you'd be the odd time and the boys laughing at you – remember how Joe laughed, Ma, and the grin of him? HAW HAW HAW!'

Joe dropped his bag at his feet and pranced about in front of the old woman, his lips stripped back from a bad mouth of teeth.

Both the priest and Josie, who had been circulating in different directions around the room, started to drift back towards Mrs McQuaid's chair.

'But you never took off the underpants,' Joe was pointing out to the old woman. 'That was the rules. Game was over then, after the boys had a good laugh at you. Till this day it was just me and Gerry at the back of the shed and Gerry decided to have a game. It was never much good with the two, but Gerry said we'd play anyway, insistent. Wouldn't let me go home until we had just one game.'

Finnegan nudged me. 'Joe's duty-free's getting away,' he whispered.

A big dark stain was spreading along the bottom of his travelling bag, something soaking through.

'And there the two of us are in a bit, both down to near the underpants. It went like that with just the two. I remember standing up trembling, reaching for the clothes. "I'm away home now, Gerry," I said. "This is no good of a game." Gerry stood up too. "I know a better one," he said. Then he grabbed me by the hair, real rough – like this.'

Joe got a handful of his own hair and yanked, his head jerking to one side.

'He looked into me face. "You're left-handed, aren't you?" he said. He took me left hand. Very gently, actually. Put it on himself. When he was pulling my pants down, he said, "You don't tell any of them at home about this game. Sure, your father's dead, anyway." Aw aye. Many's the game me and Gerry had after that.'

Mrs McQuaid's tremor had stopped.

'So, you see why I had to come, Ma? Couldn't stay away. Be like one of the Brothers at the school dying and his star pupil missing the funeral. Ingratitude, or what? Oh, and I brought you a wee something. Not right not having all of him to bury. Here's a wee something. To fill the gap in the proceedings.'

As he spat the sentences out, Joe pushed the wet bag along the floor to the old woman's feet, kick by kick. Then he stooped and whipped the zip back like a magician's trick.

'Holy fuck,' Finnegan said under his breath. 'Joe must have been the chainsaw man.'

Nothing happened for a moment or two. It was quiet, like at Mass. Then Hell broke loose.

Josie started this gasping thing, like she couldn't find her breath. Breslin – 'What the fuck? What the fuck?' – shooting up to his feet from the chair. A cup dropping somewhere, a dull thump and splash on the carpet. Josie's head jerking from the bag to the mother to Jersey Joe like a speeded-up film.

And then tiny Mrs McQuaid bending stiffly down, plunging her two veiny hands into the travelling bag.

'Go on there, Ma – lift him out,' Joe encouraged her.

Mrs McQuaid straightened back up, and the head came with her.

She had it by the ears, one in each hand, and it was dripping. Watery pink stuff, blood and melted ice mixed through one another, flowed off the rubbery skin, trickled from the closed eyes like tears, seemed to leak out of the thick, wrinkled snout like snot.

Josie's was the loudest scream. There were a few seconds when Mrs McQuaid, her mouth open and her face grey, sat back almost lazily in the chair with the pig's head sitting on her knees. It would have made a great photograph.

She took into convulsions then, a fit of rocking and jiving in the chair. But she never let go of the ears. The pig's head danced on her knee like a giddy baby. Josie grabbed her up, the two of them wailing, and got her hands free. The head fell, bumped against the stand of the coffin.

In the melee, it was the priest who got to Jersey Joe first. 'Fucking scumbag,' the priest called him – roared it into his face. Jersey Joe's head took an almighty rap on the side of the half-open door as the priest pushed him through it.

Finnegan lost it, too. A crowd had rushed in around Josie and the mother, trying to help. Finnegan started to pull and haul at them. 'Leave her alone, leave her alone,' he was shouting.

Me and Breslin went over to the head. It was resting in profile, one shut eye upwards and a wodge of thick, furry tongue poking out the side of its mouth. 'Let's get rid of this fucker,' I said.

That was some tasty operation. Breslin lifted the bag, which was swimming in its syrup of melting ice and blood, leaking its mixture out around the floor. I lifted the head by the ear and shoved it back in, splashing Breslin in the face.

We rushed our bundle out through the kitchen to the back yard, people screaming and jumping out of the way like we had a smoking bomb. We flung the bag across the yard into the side of the hedge.

'We can't leave that there,' Breslin said.

'Right,' I said. 'We'll take it back in and put it on the coffee table.'

'The dogs'll get it out here. They'll be running around the street with it tomorrow when they're taking the coffin to the chapel.'

'Right,' I said. 'We'll bury it. Get a shovel. Get the priest.'

The back door opened. It was the priest.

'Keep an eye on that cunt,' he roared, shoving Jersey Joe outside. 'If he goes to move out of the yard before the Guards arrive, break his two legs with something.'

Joe was in a sorry state. He had big scrabmarks down the side of his face where the women must have got at him. The collar was nearly ripped off his shirt.

'You fuckwit, Joe,' Breslin shouted at him. 'You'll get about ten years for that carry-on.'

'Ah Jesus, naw,' Joe protested. 'Sure, I didn't kill him. I didn't even kill the pig. One of the lads out of the bacon factory got me that.'

'He means the carry-on in there,' I told him. 'That oul woman mightn't see the morning. There'll be two for Latlurcan.'

'The Ghoul will be warming the slab for her as we're talking,' Breslin said.

'Aw . . .' Joe said. He dropped himself down onto the grass, pulled his knees up and hugged them.

He rocked there a bit, then asked, 'Were any of youse at Mammy's funeral?'

We both nodded.

'She gave me some doing in the house one time. I came home bleeding and tried to tell her all. And she bate me. But she believed me. I know she did. Bate me and believed me at the same time. Where I was they wouldn't let me home for the funeral.'

He turned his head and looked up at me.

'You played cards with The Quaid an odd time, didn't you?'

'An odd time,' I said.

'He didn't play by the rules, did he?'

'Naw,' I said. 'Gerry kind of made up his own rules, Joe.'

'He did,' Joe agreed.

He began to rummage in the pockets of his combat jacket. 'Wanna roll-up?' he asked Breslin.

'Naw, you're alright, Joe.'

He got out the tobacco and the papers. He made the papers up okay, but his hands shook so badly the tobacco went everywhere.

'Take one of these,' Breslin said, handing him a packet of Rothmans and a lighter.

'Deadly. Thanks.'

Jersey Joe blew out smoke in a long trail.

'What you suppose they'd do,' he asked, 'if they found the bold Gerry's head? Next week, or next month, say?'

'What you mean?' I asked him.

'Would they have another funeral, I mean? Like, a wee box this time.'

'Too expensive,' Breslin said. 'Josie and her oul doll'd just clear a place on the mantelpiece.'

Joe was still laughing when the Guards put him in the back of the patrol car.

'You're a funny fella, Breslin,' he called out. 'Thanks for the Rothmans.'

CROSSWALK
Jennifer Saunders

I have always wanted to be the woman
who slips into a coatroom with a stranger.
I have always wanted to be the stranger.

Woman in the closet, woman upstairs,
woman in the back of your car.

Every woman I know learned to try
to kick out a taillight if she's locked in the trunk,
to walk darkened streets
with her keys lacing her hand.

So much cramped darkness when what I want
is a penthouse, a wall of windows,
the tempered grace
of forgetting to watch my step.

Tell me how to lay me down
without counting the flights to the ground.

I can see the whole city from up here,
the taxis and the take-outs, the last-call stragglers
tumbling out of the bars. City of angels,

city of strangers, city of text-me-when-you-make-it-home.
City of her-body-was-found-in-the-park, I want
to love your roses, your seven bridges,
I want to love my name in your mouth.

I've striped my body white-on-white,
I'm holding up my hand. Your streets are full
of tents and sleeping bags, your bridges
call my name. From up here, traffic

moves so smoothly and the stars
are farther away than ever.

THE MIGHTY SALMON
Chris Burke

Hooked, beguiled, divorced from water,
here's one who'll never slap upstream
to the spawning ground, the natal river,
magnetic map, reckless muscle
raised against the foot, the kick
of dripping mountain, gravity's
dropped piano. Salmon, *salmo* in Latin,
culled from *salire* – the leaper, the jumper,
the dancer. Athlete, tail-thrasher,
tempered silver, eyes down
past twitch of talon, claw-trigger, up obstacles
dumped on scales to perfect balance,
the rapids, falls, the battle
begged, the body starved, eating itself,
unprettied now, humpbacked,
dog-toothed, rinsed-out, battered,
released from purpose, relieved to reach
the starting point and end and start it all again.

Delicious then, the way we called
our childless union off by candlelight,
returned toward our youth like adults,
raised a final, whispered fuss
and sent the salmon back upstream
to the kitchen, eagle-eyed
by every nosy diner,
in leisure, in silver splendour,
carried high and regal on a platter,
the leaper, the jumper, the dancer
undercooked on a throne of cold chips.

LASTNESS
Jed Myers

Time I confess, right here, under
the branches of this naked katsura,
its malty death scent in the air—

now while I'm surrounded by evidence
I couldn't help it. Not this autumn,
the Japanese maple in its manic flare,

the freeway's long roar a mournful rage,
allure of formlessness in the haze...
I mouth a word for it all that isn't quite

right—too bitter and I want to spit
and I wince to picture my grimacing
listener who isn't anyone yet.

Will anyone imagine this planet
a woman whose typhoon whisper starts
in her throat the magma conduits?

And her lips all the parts that can touch
other parts—raindrops and bullets,
gale-blasts against breakwaters, worn

fingernails scratching at walls? She
also isn't coming up with the right
word. But as the sea's storms'

great speaker cones wail, the fires'
crests crescendo over the foothill
developments, the gunrunners run

our young into the ground, the bees
cease in the dirt, the orcas go bony,
and knowing the white bear drowns—

I admit to it. Even these brown leaves
crinkling in swells at my feet
now chime like the highest bells

and radiate their unsealed brilliance.
What's a word for this, world shining
her first face through life's dying?

YOUR DRINKING PROBLEM
Chris Burke

Cheers. For pouring me a taste of it
still left to share, the sorry
sorry for your relapse, the spill
of news about your stay in hospital.

Thank you for your Christmas mail.
It was an agonising write, I'm sure.
A decade sober. And now I realise
the measure of the flood you dammed.

No, not that. How you felt it near,
the ripened water breathing at your door,
the torture of its sickly heartbeat
like a leaky tap at night. Dear friend,

you were the better man. And now
you're in the deep end of my leisure pool.
Drown. Swim. Get out. I write this sorry
jetsam drunk and absolutely staggering.

THE CROATIAN
Marie Coveney

Tall stranger lunges into their mornings
hair matted with sand and salt spray
eyes reddened from drinking wood-wine.

He teeters towards a bench of old men
hands over sticks, heads drawn together.
They talk of the glut of figs in the old town

the delights of their wives' *Crostata di Fichi*.
He stretches a hand for some coins, they point
to Sperlonga's whitewashed towers

'plenty of figs for the taking up there.' He sways
then climbs the stone risers.
A glaring of feral cats feast on leftovers:

orecchiette glistening with ragu, ricotta oozing
from tubes of cannelloni.
He hunts them away to the fig trees.

Sated, he stands, salutes prickly pears —
the green men of the slopes
but the sun beats down and his body slumps.

Around him lie fruits, squashed under foot
or blackened and fermenting. From the red innards
of a fig, a bee staggers.

LAST RITES
Cian Ferriter

Uncle Jack once gripped a man's half-severed hands
while giving him last rites in Santiago;
bullets puffing dirt from broken ground,
clothes strung above them in the narrow street
like echoes of the dead or missing.

He gave up speech at last; sought answers
in what leaked through night-time's cracks;
a bare bulb flickering in his top-floor flat;
dawn-light catching the sides of ashtrays;
cats tip-toeing between bottles.

'A man who put others before himself'
who fell holding out his hands to rain,
to his shadow opening large to meet him,
to love on the other side, waiting,
to clay returning without interest to clay.

COTTON RATS
Justin Hunt

Sumner County, Kansas, July 1960

They seemed to come from nowhere:
swarm after furry swarm—half-starved,
scuttered up from Texas, the old men said.

Out by the rodeo grounds, they flurried
from culverts, scampered the road
with baby-fist feet, swirled like flocks
of wingless starlings into fields of stubble,
gleaned every last head of uncut wheat.

A mile north, at Cranmers' place,
they clustered in the chicken coop,
gnawed its timbers day and night—
until my best friend and I, armed with rakes,
stormed in one morning, beat on walls
and drove the rats outside, where
most escaped to the brush behind the barn,
though scores scurried to shelter
in the cast-iron pipes we'd laid as traps.

We strutted out, tipped up the pipes
one by one, and with our rakes'
hickory handles churned the rodents
to pulp, piled them high in the yard,
proud of our work—no thought
for the way a life looks for cover,
comes to an end one mercy short.

Awful Things
Kathryn Merwin

Live-wire, sparking warnings in the street: everybody
wanted to touch you. Wanted to drink

your blood. I'll spend another night untouched
and think of you, turning in and out

of your mind. Molting, snake-like, in the strange silence
of one body betraying another. I know what you felt —

how it tunneled through your body. How it bit
into your liver. Broke your Arizona heart.

In the west, your mother is filling a bath tub.

Your father is smoking a long cigar. But you filled yourself
with kerosene, lit the match with the flame you coughed

up like blood on your pillowcase:
something in your chest is ticking. There were pretty words

left to say, but now it's grown dark. November only remembers
the snow, not the dead beneath it. It was darkness that gave you a taste

for light. And here you are, now, whispering through radio-static. Tell me
how to unlearn this language. Tell me awful things.

LOVE POEM
Katherine Noble

I want you to understand the German fairy tales.
You are standing in the woods. It is December.
The sky is a poison arrow arcing at your heart.
The sky is crippled with rooks, witches mooning
blue, ugly faces. I am in our cabin, far.
There is a fire burning in anticipation.
I am cutting off my fingers for the days you are gone.
I am singing soft and out of key. I am drowning
so many cats. You have slayed innumerable things.
Night falls. You hear wolves, captives, close
lightning. There is no road.
Your horse will be maimed by morning.
You must kill it
or carry it. There is no other way home.

IN THE HOUSE, I BUILT ANOTHER HOUSE,
Melissa Studdard

and that was my body,
made of wine, pills, and regret.
Made of cigarettes and self-blame.
Smoke and baby cries
leaked from all the windows.
The baby's face was a red fist
punching nothing.
Then the doctor said *pregnant*,
and I said *I'll never be good enough.*
And the doctor said,
The baby is not yet a baby.
I said, *I am the baby.*
I went home and built another house,
one that my husband could not enter.
A fortress of withdrawal.
He drank for both of us.
I started making bones.

WHEN MY LOVER SAYS HIPPOPOTOMONSTROSESQUIPPEDALIOPHOBIA,
Melissa Studdard

I say, *It's not fear that matters, but where*
you bury it. So he buries his
tongue inside me, and I tell him that sometimes I'm more afraid
of hearing what I know
than knowing it. I want to lick the vowels out of all words
longer than three syllables. I want to find every horse
led against its will into battle and tie it to a cloud.
What god said to the wind to make it bend the daffodils,
they also said to my lover's lips.
And I turn over and over
in the field of myself.
Tell me, who never wakes up afraid?
When Jesus asked if he really had to,
god showed up dressed in yellow petals and
handed him a crown of thorns.
Don't make me say what I'm willing to do for love.
I'm already lugging my cross up the hill.

LISTEN
Leslie Williams

Spring coming in like cochlear implants
that's how close I'd like to be
burrowed in your ear canal
I hear Adidas shoes are fashionable again
in the eighties boys said it was an acronym
for *All Day I Dream About Sex*
maybe they didn't say *acronym* but everyone knew
what they meant and that every dream's a need
to re-integrate parts that drifted away
just as dreaming of an old-fashioned telephone
means some ideas are antiquated but still there to be received
and may be necessary when invited to another wedding
it's possible the cobblestones will remember me
though the daffodils will be of a new generation
this is not the time I'm going to understand anything

*

There are turkeys mating in the yard right now
some of the hens pecking each other
waiting their turn
the tom comes over to get involved
I feel I should avert my eyes to give them privacy
have you seen this the hen lies down in the middle of the crowd
and the dominant tom stands on her back
puts both of those turkey-leg feet with three splayed toes
on top of her but before anything else happens
another tom rushes over and stops it
which makes no sense because wouldn't you be in favor of
your species continuing but then there are your particular genes
to fight for

*

It's ridiculous to remember in such detail
the man and woman dream
talking quietly he leaned in and she pulled away
he said *I'm sorry* and she said *no don't be* and kissed him back
then he needed to take the call on a landline
it was kind of a power thing
the woman didn't stop to complain because he had already
made her happy and she loved being thrown back
to more scintillating times
he said *we are almost done here* but she didn't know if
he was saying it to the woman on the phone or
to the woman she now was.

SISTERS-IN-LAW
Mary Woodward

After "Dialogue between Fashion and her sister Death" by Giacomo Leopardi

Death is the sworn enemy of memory says Leopardi but
she exists still in fragments: a red and white flowered
Cacherel dress hanging in their windowless bathroom

one hot London August weekend of Greek meals and
white wine; or in a grey wool Stephen Marks jacket with
a back of godets, swinging ahead along a Tube platform –

a month's wages, she laughed, our standard phrase for ruin;
or dark jeans and a pastel blue cashmere sweater, hair
cut and hennaed at Leonard's, the highest heels sold in

Sacha Shoes. You never make mistakes, she told me as if
she always got things wrong. Like Fashion and her slower
sister, we had much in common, daughters of Frailty,

terrified of standing still. *Keep moving*: that spider-web
voice had trained us well: no such thing as permanence,
no colour, no form, no texture you can trust for ever.

Even her loyally loved perfume – Miss Balmain –
has been discontinued. When I asked for it in Selfridges
the French salesgirl in the black suit shook her head,

smiled and asked if I'd like to try the new one. Anyway
I had Fracas on my wrist from the Isabella Blow show –
sufficient tuberose reminder of how darkly things go on.

Mea Culpa
Carlo Gébler

I

I was born in 1954. So this year* I turned 65 and embarked on my 66th year on earth.

Now, given the year what's in it, the British state, which previously only ever communicated either to ask for money, or to tell me I was in trouble, has been bombarding me with bits of paper connected to this calendrical milestone.

First there was the letter from social security in Newcastle, where pensions in the UK are organised from. Dear Karl the letter began, for I am known to our friends in the north by my baptismal moniker, your pension will be coming only not when you expected, i.e., now you've got to 65. Owing to a shortage of funds, it's being postponed a bit.

I was, I must say, not in the least bit miffed to receive this. In fact I was actually quite pleased. If the pension were deferred then that meant OAP-hood was deferred too, didn't it? Yes, I thought so. Technically I might be 65 and pensionable but really I wasn't. Or so I kept telling meself (and I've had a lifetime's practice in that department. Denial – I'm world class, pal.)

Next there was the communiqué from the Belfast health board containing the bowel cancer self-tester kit. Emulating Mrs Beeton's recipe for jugged hare ("First catch your hare…") the instructions began, "First catch your stool…" Once caught, the instructions continued, I was to use a wooden spatula (a fistful were provided) to dab some stool into a pair of recessed cardboard reservoirs. I was then to repeat this procedure over successive days, dabbing more stool into other reservoirs, dating each entry of course (this was a fiendishly complicated process) and, once the task was complete, I was to send everything back to them in the special leak-proof self-addressed envelope they'd thoughtfully provided. If it turned out something was wrong, my GP would be in touch. Otherwise *nada*. That's what the letter said.

*Written in October 2019

I did as I was told but heard nothing from the GP and, I have to say, I wasn't just pleased about that, I was elated. Not hearing meant 'it' hadn't happened, and seeing as 'it' only happened to the old, this meant I wasn't old, yet.

Then came the letter about my first ever flu jab, which I was offered of course because of having attained the big six five, and on receipt of which I found myself obliged to perform a very complicated psychological fandango. Your health, said the professional hypochondriac inside, your health is good and, in the normal run of things, you shouldn't need to have this jab. You're not so old. However, Mr Hypochondriac continued, seeing as you're going back into the prisons to work (I am) and seeing as the wings are rotten with germs (who knows if they actually are, but I have always been susceptible to this particular poisonous fantasy), you should do this, to protect yourself, though that's nothing to do with the age thing... You're still really not a crock, yet.

Impeccable logic from himself, I thought and with a lightly fluttering heart I made an appointment for my jab one early afternoon on a Thursday in late September.

The Thursday came. I entered the health centre where my GP's practice is based: I was a working man, still in his prime...

Inside, humming neon lights, a warren of rooms and corridors, the sick lounging about, (Crikey I hate the sick, I thought, sauntering past them), the special surgery smell (disinfectant, baked radiator dust, witch hazel), which hasn't changed since childhood, and counters with receptionists (all inscrutable) who also seem unchanged since childhood.

I found my GP's reception desk and, as I had been instructed, I said I was there for the jab. Then I added that I'd sit and wait in the usual waiting area.

"No, sorry," said the receptionist, "but would you mind not sitting in the general waiting area."

What! I was looking forward to leafing through an ancient copy of *Ulster Tatler*, a publication I only ever see at the doctor's. I particularly like the pictures, which are always to be found in the *Tatler*, of the province's bourgeoisie in their best frocks and tuxedos at Marie Curie fund raisers and Rotarian dinners. I like them because these photographs allow me to sneer and nothing puts snap in my celery like a good sneer. Frankly, it's really the only thing I enjoy when I come to see the doctor – (everything else about the doctor is hideous) – looking at the *Ulster Tatler* and sneering at the Ulster bourgeoisie. And if I understood correctly, I was now being denied this pleasure?

My eyebrows rose. The receptionist waved at the corner behind me. "Please go and sit over there and Hermione will collect you when she's ready."

Hermione will collect me? What, like a parcel?

I didn't actually say that. I just said, "Hermione will collect me?" in my best ironically inflected Hugh Grant voice.

"Yes, Karl, Hermione will do that when she's ready. So take a seat, Karl. Hermione will be along presently."

People with authority, I've noticed, typically revert to the exclusive use of forenames in only two circumstances: either when you're an infant or when you're an oldie, which was what, seemingly, as far as this receptionist was concerned, I was. Really?

The receptionist returned to the keyboard and I turned to see where I was supposed to go. OMG. It was the corner by the double doors which led the toilet, i.e., in health centre terms, it was Siberia; and it was packed with old people, all of whom looked like dry, wrinkled prunes. And I was supposed to sit with them, in public?

I settled into a seat in the middle of the OAP corral, then raised my *Guardian* high to screen my face. If I wasn't seen by anybody passing then it followed I wasn't part of this ancient crew. Yes, I know, magical thinking, but it worked for me.

The minutes ticked by, then Hermione's door was flung open and there she was, sprightliness incarnate.

"Malcolm," she said.

Malcolm crept into Hermione's surgery and a few minutes later crept back out again and came up to us. His jacket buttons were comically misaligned.

"Didn't cry, so I didn't," he announced for our collective benefit. "Brave boy aren't I?"

I didn't laugh. Nobody did. Something had to be said about the buttons, though, so I said it.

"Buttons," I said. Malcolm dropped his head and saw his front buttons were in the wrong button holes.

"Oh," Malcolm said.

Malcolm began to undo the first button. His hands were shaking so much that in the time it took him to get the first button back out through its slit, I could easily have written a haiku. Or two.

"Stop with the fucking buttons," I wanted to shout but instead I ventured, "Shall I help?"

"No," Malcolm said calmly. "I prefer to do it myself." I prefer to do it myself. Holy Hell.

Hermione was at her door again and this time it was a trio who responded to her summons, two ancient parents plus their almost but not quite as ancient son. I found this family ensemble obscene: I mean, a whole nest of oldies? I mean there's disgusting and then there's disgusting.

The trio shuffled off and in, and we who were left watched as Malcolm, with painful difficulty, undid two more jacket buttons. Then he did them all up again and of course, of course — when he did them up again, they were all bloody wrong weren't they. I didn't say anything. Nobody said anything. What would have been the point? We'd all have just had to sit and watch as he did the same thing again. It would have been like watching Tantalus in Hades failing to get his drink, over and over again.

Eventually, my name was called. I went into the surgery and sat opposite Hermione.

"You're here for the wee flu jab?"

"Yes."

"And would you like an extra wee jab for the pneumonia and the meningitis?"

If the use of wee once was bad, its double use was intolerable. Why are the jabs wee? I wanted to ask. Do you think I'm a frightened wee child? I said nothing of course. I just smiled and said, "I'll have both. Thank you, that would be lovely." My irony wasn't noticed.

A minute later, having been pricked twice (and no, it didn't hurt, it was just two wee jabs) I emerged from Hermione's lair.

One of the waiting old, just outside the door, was a red-faced fellow in a hideous tomato-red windcheater, the colour of which definitely did not match his pallor.

"Anything strange to report?" he asked me.

I knew immediately what he was up to. He was trying to provoke me into talking because if he got me talking that would bind me into the group: he was also doing the other thing, the making-common-cause thing: he was trying to make out I was one of them, and he wanted me to know I was one of them and he wanted me to agree I was one of them, but I was having none of it. Absolutely not. No way, José.

"No, nothing strange to report," I said and fled. Nobody was getting me in this club. Not as long as I was breathing.

2

Saturday morning, a few days later. I had go to Dublin for a literary festival. I took the train to Connolly and then switched to the DART which would bring me to the suburb where the festival was taking place.

The train was rammed and the only seat was a window seat beside an old man with a viola in a case. The viola was on the empty seat beside him. This is the sort of thing that makes me very annoyed. "On a full train you can't put your viola on the seat, mate." That's what I wanted to say. What I actually said was, "Is there any chance I could squeeze in there?" He took the viola onto his lap and I wriggled in. I didn't sense he was best pleased. A few stops later, the carriage emptied out a bit. He moved to the seat opposite and I got a good look at him.

He had an interwar moustache and thin thighs. The thighs were like sickles lurking inside his corduroys. He had dentures too, top and bottom. These kept slipping and he had to keep pushing them back into place with his tongue and every time he did this there was a noise. I could hear it plainly above clatter of the carriage. It was a noise like a Morse code generator might make, but more random and more irritating. Click, click... click, click...

"Stop with clicking," I wanted to shout, but as we have already established I'm too middle-class for that kind of malarkey.

Just before what I would discover was his stop he pronounced, *sotto voce*, "All yours now." Then the DART stopped and he padded unsteadily on his stick-thin, sickle-like legs out the door and onto the platform and away towards the exit, cradling his musical instrument case at the bottom with both hands and pulling it into his chest. God I hated him, preening old codger.

"Hey, mate," I felt like shouting, "there's a handle. Use the bloody handle..."

He'd been infuriating, but now he was gone, I realised I had an opportunity, which I seized with gusto, for a self-serving thought, and hey, there's no better thought than a self-serving one.

He and I might have been the same age. We were certainly near enough. But compare us and it would be obvious. We weren't in the same category. Look at the moustache for a start. Well, that said it all, didn't it. Only an oldie would commit a style crime like that. I wouldn't, nay couldn't, which meant, I was not nearly as old as he was. Reasons to be cheerful, one, two, three...

3

A few hours later, towards the end of the session at the literary festival I had come to Dublin to attend (a panel discussion, three speakers plus a chair), a heckler shouted out from the audience, "Rubbish, you're talking rubbish..." The heckler used the rubbish word several times and was quite emphatic about this. We'd all been talking rubbish, me included, or perhaps even me particularly. The charge was fiercely put but what I noticed as I sat, the denunciation washing about me, was that my heart *wasn't* racing, my palms *weren't* sweaty and my mouth *wasn't* dry, which say a year before they all would have been.

And hecklers always coming, as we know, like buses, in pairs, no sooner had the first finished, but a second started. We had ruined everything, the second heckler said. We'd introduced filthy politics and sown discord and offence. Again, the vilification went on for quite a while and again what I noticed was that my heart *wasn't* racing and my palms *weren't* sweaty and my mouth *wasn't* dry. For the first time ever, and I've had my share of hecklers believe you me, the body evinced no signs of anxiety at a heckler's heckle. Not a scintilla.

Interesting that, I thought, but how come? Why were the traditional responses to public disparagement not showing themselves? It had never happened before. I had no idea. But something was up.

4

A bit later, sitting on platform 4 at Connolly Station – it was a miserable evening with the tail of Hurricane Lorenzo battering the glass roof above – I pondered my reaction and was struck by a revolutionary thought.

Over the years I had often heard old people say, "You know the amazing thing about getting old is you stop caring about the opinions of others. You become indifferent to them. They don't like what you say, they don't like what you believe: it might have mattered once, but it doesn't matter to you now. You simply stop caring." One oldie had put it in nautical terms, which I remembered now: "When people are unpleasant and heap obloquy on your head," this oldie had said (and the use of obloquy in everyday conversation guaranteed, of course, that these words would be remembered), "you just jump into your dingy, round the headland and vanish out to sea."

Could it be, I now wondered, that what I had been told about had miraculously become my SOP? Only this new arrangement, because I'd been so fiercely determined to assert I wasn't changing, I wasn't ageing, and I was still my young self, had come into place without my noticing. Could that be right?

5

A couple of days following my epiphany on the dank platform at Connolly, I bumped into a writer. This writer was a friend but on Grub Street all friends are also rivals and every interaction is rotten with envy. At least that has always been the case in my life, so far.

We fell to talking and my friend/rival, (he could hardly control himself actually) began to speak of a novel (his) and his recent, colossal good fortune in relation to his novel: my friend/rival having recently completed said novel had just sold it for a large sum (mouth-watering) to a UK publisher: and now my friend/rival was in conversation with his adoring UK publisher about the jacket, the publication date, the novel's imminent auction at the Frankfurt Book Fair, the upcoming book tour and even the launch party. The Ivy, in London, seemingly. Or else the Groucho, if the Ivy wasn't free.

As I listened I waited and what I was waiting for was what always happened in such situations, the deep but powerful throb of envy surging below the solar plexus, and which, for as long as I had lived and breathed, had never failed to make its appearance when I learnt that others were doing better than me; in this case, me who had not written a novel, had not sold it to a UK publisher for a mouth-watering sum, et cetera, et cetera. But nothing happened. No envy throb stabbed below.

After my friend/rival and I parted company, I checked exhaustively within to see if there was even a small hot ember of envy glowing malevolently under a blanket of ash.

But I found nothing. Nothing. Now I really was puzzled. What's happening? I wondered. My whole life had been shot through with envy. It was a defining emotion. It was also, as I knew from my own experience, a lasting emotion. It lingered. Oh yes, it hung about. Sometimes for years, even decades. But today, nothing. For the first time ever, in sixty-five years of envying, it hadn't shown up and there was no sign it would either.

6

In the 1970s I knew a couple of Italian anarchists slightly and mostly what they spoke about (at least this is what I remember) was the state and the deep state and the difference between the two.

The state, they said, was what you saw. The state did the bins and set the speed limits on the *autostrada*. The deep state, on the other hand, they did the forward planning and you never saw them or what they did until after they'd done it, unless of course you were an anarchist because if you were an anarchist you were able to see these things because well, anarchists could.

It all made sense back then and amazingly it was making sense again now. In the recent past, I realised, I'd taken every intimation of age (the pension letter, the bowel cancer thingee, the flu jab invitation) and spun it to mean the reverse because that was the way to assert I wasn't an old un. Meantime, the deep psyche had decided, now I was 65 and had reached my majority, so to speak, that my ancient anxiety in the face of hostility and my bottomless envy when others succeeded and I did not, were both now surplus to requirements. They could go, the deep psyche resolved, and their decision made, they did away with them. But I only found out after the change had been made that these things that had hobbled me all my life had been dumped and had been replaced with the kind of "I don't give a damn" serenity which I had heard the old talk of but had never believed would come to my estate.

But they had, they have, and I am happy, extremely happy that they have, and now it only remains that I seek out the man in the red windcheater, whom I met at my GP's, he whom I spurned when he tried, in his own lovely way, to welcome me to the fold, and profess before him my mea culpa.

"I'm sorry," I will say, "I'm sorry I rejected your overture, but now I am ready to make common cause. I will get a red windcheater. I might try and grow an interwar moustache. And next year, when I go back to the surgery for my flu jab, I won't have to be told to sit in the special OAP corral with you and others. I'll take myself there voluntarily. Just you wait and see. I'm one of you now and I'm sorry, so sorry, it's taken me so long to admit it."

FOUR POEMS
Dean Browne

THE EMIGRÉ

Upturn the bucket of sand on the bedroom floor and spread your fingers
in the ground shell and seaglass – right up to your wrists
until you've shaped a beach between the skirting-board and bookcase.
Tape down tarpaulin cut from your old tent sticky with pine sap, and
pour the plastic bottle of salt water in the hollow for the sea.
Crêpe crimped at specific points, scored with a pin and suspended
by a shoelace from the ceiling will represent the seagull.
A clipping from your poppy red scarf will represent the crab,
a raw egg, jellyfish. Step on it barefoot – there is no pain here.
Next sow the tiny fishing boats along the shore: stove in,
windows streaked as if with tears, the starboards like scratchcards. Scrape

gunge away with your fingernail and find a girl's name, *Grace*
or *Kate S 609*, a goitre tangled squid-like in the fishnets.
Spark up your last cigarette – do not burn the gull. You can be patient
or you can be patient. Soon a vessel will advance in the shallows.
Attract the captain's eye, and, if he knew your father, he'll ferry you across
that brief body of water to the island on the other side – where,
at low tide, you can unscrew mussels from stone; watch them nose
from their doors, poached in a saucepan with herbs and *Marques de Riscal*.
You'll watch from a rock the chickens poking around the seaweed –
russet feathers pearled with spray, their eyes freaked with fierce sea-green –
the rosa rugosa, a baby seal, until one silver hair shows in your fringe.

THE TRIANGLE

I should never have written the instruction manual
illustrating the 52 distinct tones that can be struck
from the triangle, popular now in concert halls
from here to Berlin. It's brought me nothing but success.

The joke, at first, was exquisite as a devilled egg
and the expression on their faces like a sweet pimento.
You put the phony in symphony tonight, grinned back
the shiny hand-dryer in the gents. Gobs dropped

and I went on, describing the point tapped just so
for the blackbird's dawn trill, the ripple on a clear lake
in Sweden, the squeak of gas that jets from a burning coal.
One tone only audible to toddlers, another only to dogs.

Of course I reddened when those rich fools Googled me,
the search results proved it true. The hits were legion.
Not only that, the book had entered its fourth print run
and was forthcoming in Russian translation.

That's when it occurred to me that I was late
to deliver the keynote address at the annual summit
for lovers of the triangle, my lecture on the sweeter octaves
of beryllium copper – how to damp it for the rustle

like the train of a bridal dress trailed over cobbles.
Or pitch it like the mice celebrating the owl's demise
by lightning, or the *ting!* so crystalline it's called frost creeping.
So I jotted some notes, grabbed my jacket, and said *taxi*.

KINTSUGI

After the world ends, there's still the washing-up
to do. That last meal, *arrabiata*, meaning
'anger', she says. Illuminated by the soft, violet stone
of the salt lamp more tested and tarnished on one side
than the other, each pushes about the plate. Some objects fade
before they vanish. Though never with the closure
of a slammed door when they go. Sooner than he thinks
it is time to make coffee in the French Press
she bought, and survey, from the weathered suitcase, what
remains of a life. Like whittling spalted bark
of pitch pine on a sagging porch until what's left
is a splinter, operatic pulse under the skin
of the thumb. Such poor broken things, flowering jags,
exciting care in the handling.
One morning he may go out and thrushes, picking
on the ground, will startle back to the bare bush
like a smashed glass reassembling
that stands then, astonished by itself.

ECLECTUS

What starts it is the Eclectus parrot, named Hannah,
her free-range cock-eyed hop along Wolfe Tone Square,
her unlikely garb of crimson affecting smart casual –
'what business has live poultry doing here?' –
and for once it occurs to me I should ring the father.
We both own phones, do we not? Yet the dead line
fans out between us like an aspirant sapling,
screening each from the other these last few years.
His chicken coops have come down with a lazy shower
of cherry blossoms. See him unlatch the flights, stoop
through low doors, dish seeds, chopped pomegranate
and nuts to the birds he breeds, their feathers hi-vis,
eyes live wired. *Violet is a mutation of blue* he says,
and his prized Indian Ringnecks strut their genes.
The father is offering glosses on *cleartails, lacewings*, all
I hear are the words. Grateful he is speaking. *Son.*
See him touch the flushed, mango plumage of a sun conure,
a black-headed caique he calls 'the Republican', perched
on his shoulder. Welsummers, rosellas, frilled bantam silkies
need him. One parrot glows foxfire green. The father
reaches in and it shuffles onto his open palms, enters
mine, to its and my surprise. See my thumbs cup the wings,
as though this one thing might be kept good between us.

CHAMOMILE
Cristina Ioana Aramă

I remember her hands trembled on a Sunday morning after she swallowed five codeines. She'd taken them to forget that she'd never be good enough for me. I made her promise not to take any more.

I remember she only drank a specific brand of water, and preferred cream cheese with no dill. She always drank a cup of coffee in the morning, paired with a Marlboro Red.

I remember that the first time we went out for tea, she wanted to meet at the statue of Spiru Haret at the University of Bucharest, to associate it with me. I was wearing a turtleneck she always called "maletă", and a gray wool coat.

I remember she walked in long strides, bending her knees and bouncing with each step. She told me that she would've liked to have been able to fly. She wanted to see the cities from above.

I remember her father told her that if he ever caught her with a girl, he'd mutilate her. Break her legs and cut her tendons. Her mother liked to threaten she'd tell him about me.

I remember she talked in verse and wrote poetry in a journal with a Bic ballpoint pen. She pressed chamomile, pansies and rose petals and taped them between poems. Sometimes, she left some aside. She picked them up very delicately and gave them to me.

I remember she loved biking and going on long hikes, and had an oval scar on the side of her knee from the time her ligament split and she got surgery to stick it back. When she woke up from the anesthesia, she didn't know that the dark orange stain on her leg was iodine and worried that she'd gotten her period. The doctor said that from then on she'd have to do leg exercises each morning. She couldn't ride a bike or go hiking again.

I remember she had a shelf bursting with Christian books her mother had made her read, and even though he beat his wife bloody, her father insisted on taking the children to church every Sunday.

I remember her mother told her she should've aborted her.

I remember she called me one morning to say she couldn't get out of bed because her leg wouldn't bend. The night before, her mother had forced her to pray on her knees. Whenever she heard about her daughter's legs hurting, she shrugged and said she deserved it, and that lesbians had sex with dildos in the shape of the holy cross.

I remember she hated fresh flowers and movies because every time her parents fought, her father brought her mother a bouquet and took the children to the cinema.

I remember she went to Alcoholics Anonymous before we met. It was during the time she poured a small bottle of vodka into her coffee before school and jumped the fence to buy beer at Mega Image.

I remember her father asked her if she had any cocaine, and told her to share it with him if she did.

I remember she believed her death would be grandiose. She rarely checked for cars before crossing the street, didn't care about getting lung cancer, and never worried about the elevator crashing.

I remember that she wouldn't be able to carry a child. She made up for it by taking care of her brothers, hugging them and kissing them on the forehead whenever her mother shouted at them.

I remember that when her art teacher had the class paint a saint of their choice on a piece of glass, she painted a cigarette.

I remember I started pressing flowers too and giving them to her. The first one I pressed was an orchid, but it grew mold. Then I gave her chamomile, rhododendrons and apple blossoms. I still have violet petals in my wallet between two credit cards from when I had no book on me to press them in.

I remember she insisted I take a drag of her cigarette whenever she smoked in my kitchen. What eventually made her cut down on smoking was that I picked it up too.

She disagrees with me on this, but I remember that the first time we met, she was wearing a blue jacket. It was October.

I remember she punched walls when she was angry and rubbed the blood off with baby wipes. After she met me, though, her raging fits got rarer. When she fought with her mother, she didn't scream or pace around the room anymore.

I remember she told me the people who came to Alcoholics Anonymous were some of the most grounded and hard-working people she'd ever met.

I remember that the last time I read her poems, the chamomile was missing.

I remember that from a certain point on, she began looking both ways before crossing the street. She stopped assuring me the elevator wouldn't crash.

And I remember that eventually, after I left, she gave up her Marlboro Reds.

CAN YOU FEEL IT?
Shelley Hastings

We booked a weekend in Berlin on our credit cards. I was bored and miserable, working in a discount clothes shop on the Holloway Road, living in an attic room in a large shared house. I was nineteen and waiting for something to happen that meant something. Leah suggested it one lunchtime at work. She was thin and tall, at least a foot above me, and trying to get into modelling. She said she wanted to go to Berlin because of the alternative scene.

'The Germans are into my look,' she said holding her chin up, 'and the flights are cheap.'

'Sounds good.'

I finished my crisps, then my sandwich and tossed the packets in the bin. Leah looked at me, twisting the stud in her nose with the end of her nail.

'Well?'

'Well what?'

She unwrapped some gum and curled it into her mouth. 'Come on babe. Don't be lame. I thought you said you wanted to do something different.' She leant back on her chair, chewing slowly.

'Yeah, I do.' I looked up at the clock above the door and then at the rota on the board. My lunchbreak was over. My chest felt tight. She was still staring at me. 'Okay, sure. We can have a look anyway.'

The night before we flew, I sat at the bathroom sink, put on latex gloves and dyed my hair, 'Flaming Red'. The colour took in clumps, some sections darker than others, pale orange underneath. I tied it up to make it look okay. I cut in a short fringe with the kitchen scissors and put in round black studs. It framed my face, I looked better. Older. Braver than I felt.

At Gatwick we sat on high stools and Leah ordered oysters and champagne. Her eyes were heavy with make-up, her dark hair spilling over the counter, her bangles glinting down her arms. The man at the stand topped up our glasses without charging us. I watched Leah narrow her eyes at him then throw her head back and slurp from the shell. I swilled the briny taste in my mouth, chewed, gagged, then swallowed. Then I clinked her glass. 'Cheers!'

'Cheers! It feels like we might never come back,' Leah said. I smiled and downed my drink, then followed her to the gate high from the fizz.

Berlin was the coldest place I had ever been. My raincoat was thin, and I hadn't packed enough clothes. Even with layers it cut through. Our hostel was tall and grey with tiny windows and a bar in the basement. The city felt raw compared to London, like it was under construction. The first day, Leah made us jump over a fence into a derelict wasteland to take photos. I held the camera while she climbed the scaffolding. I was nervous she might slip, but she sat, legs dangling, balanced on a ridge. She was dwarfed by a concrete skeleton, steel rods rusting out its ends, her thin body the only life.

In the afternoon we walked to Hamburger Bahnhof, a gallery in an old railway station, and Leah posed next to the neon strips that lined the outside. It was starting to get dark and she looked ghostly blue, her cheekbones blurry, her eyes shiny red pricks in the tiny image on my camera.

We spent the first evening in the hostel bar. The whole place was full of young European backpackers, well turned out, Spanish students with good teeth and tennis shoes. We were both in black with dark lipstick, me in tight jeans and DM boots and Leah towering over me in a Lycra dress, our hair knotted up with elastic bands. The resident DJ, a sweaty Scot who ran the drinking games, called out to us over the microphone.

'Willkommen ladies! Which one of you is gonna bring the DJ a smoke?'

He sent shots of tequila to our table and told us nothing decent in Berlin happened until after midnight. 'I only play this disco shite here because I'm paid to.' He was short and stocky, and wearing a string vest with a thick silver chain like a bike lock around his neck.

'What scene you into?' he said.

'Not this,' Leah said, waving her cigarette at the dancefloor.

'I'll take you out somewhere real, pal,' he said.

'Maybe tomorrow,' Leah said, sticking her fingers down her throat when his back was turned. We ordered vodka and Leah started talking to this tattooed Italian guy in leather trousers. She was swivelling her hips, her arms on his shoulders. They couldn't keep their hands off each other. She disappeared to the loo and when she came back she told me she had just sucked him off in the communal showers.

'You what?'

'What's the problem?' She was laughing.

'No problem.' I looked at her mouth as she lit another cigarette and then she told me that he had a motorbike and wanted to take her for a tour of the city at night.

'Right now?'

She took my face in her hands and stuck out her bottom lip. 'Come on, babe. Relax. See you back here in a bit?'

'Alright.'

She leaned over and whispered in my ear, 'Be good!'

'Yeah, okay.'

I watched her go and then stood smoking, watching everyone else dance. I ordered a beer and looked at the posters pasted along the bar, picking at the edges, peeling bits off and rolling them into balls between my fingers. I thought about Leah, pulling on her helmet and speeding away, her arms wrapped around his waist.

When the Scot finished his set, he handed out flyers telling everyone to follow him to Bunker, a techno club in the middle of the city.

'You coming, pal?'

'No, I don't think so. Maybe later.'

People started to leave, and I stood in the fluorescent light of the lobby next to the lift fiddling with my dorm key. At the last minute I pulled on my coat and followed them. I trailed the Spanish boys getting on and off the yellow trams, and then followed the crowd heading towards the searchlights that shot up through the sky.

The club was in a large square concrete building, an ex-air raid shelter. There were food vans dotted along the road playing dance music on tinny radios. My boots skidded on the icy pavement. I dug my hands deep into my pockets and joined the back of the queue. By then I didn't know where anyone from the hostel had gone. The guy on the door had short dreadlocks and a long leather coat. He was wearing a silver metal glove like a knight. I wondered if underneath it something was wrong with his hand, if he'd put it in a fire.

Inside it was packed. Hot and dark. People were half-dressed, tattooed, with leather studded collars and pierced faces. The techno was loud, relentless, hundreds of bodies moving, fists pumping, heads nodding. Lasers flashed across the ceiling. Nobody was talking, everybody was dancing. I tied my coat around my waist and then stood in a corner, my fingertips touching the damp walls, just watching. The bass was so loud I could feel it in my jaw. There was a banner behind the DJ that said 'TERROR'. Bodies were slick with sweat, which was rising to the ceiling and dripping down. I pulled out my cigarettes, lit one and stood hidden in the steamy darkness, taking it all in. I thought about Leah and what she would think if she knew I was here. I went to look for the bar, bought a beer and then I went to the toilet. People were out of it, sat all over the floor and on the sinks, faces gurning. I climbed over them and then sat on the loo with one foot wedged against the door to stop anyone walking in on me. When I came out, I looked in the mirror, and in the pink light of the bathroom I looked different. I touched my hair, my new short fringe. I washed my hands and put on more lipstick. A woman in a halter neck pointed at my drink so I gave it to her, and she swigged it quickly, then wiped her mouth. Her hands were shaking.

'Are you okay?' I offered her the beer again. She smiled at me. 'Danke.' Then she handed me a blue pill with a tiny white bird pressed into the top and touched her tongue. She was watching me, so I put it in my mouth and washed it down.

When I went back out projections were filling the back wall. Everything was flickering in time to the music. I went up the metal stairs to stand on the balcony and watch from above. I held onto the rail and looked at the mass of people dancing below me, their flashing limbs. The films were a montage of black and white news footage of men in suits. Politicians I didn't know getting off planes and shaking hands. Riot police in helmets, pushing back protesters. Bombs dropping through the sky like giant swollen fish. Mushroom clouds exploding. I let go of the rail and, aware of my body, started to dance. People had their arms raised up, their faces staring at the ceiling. Air horns were sounding. The music was overwhelming. It felt like they were all one fleshy machine and they all knew what they were doing. Something fell away inside of me, so I closed my eyes and kept moving.

When I opened them, the projections had changed to old movies. Laurel and Hardy. Their legs waddling, eyebrows going, hats flying. I was smiling. Everyone was smiling. Children sat on swings, their legs in the air, rising and falling. A gospel choir was singing. Then the back wall filled with mountains and sky and clouds billowing and the man dancing next to me held his arms up like he was praying. I stopped for a moment. I knew something profound was happening. Birds soared across the dark brick of the building and I felt the roar of the music and everyone's hearts beating. I thought about my job, and about my attic room at home. I thought about how I was here, in Berlin, and this was happening to me, how this meant something. I couldn't hold on to why, but I raised my arms up too and the praying man next to me smiled and gave me his bottle of water. The cold trickled though me. I am here, I thought, and it's going to be alright. I cried with relief. The man leaned into me and touched my shoulder. I shook my head at him and smiled. 'I'm good,' I said, then wiped my tears into my sweat and kept dancing.

After a long time, I started to see the edges of things. The space became lighter, people were leaving. I looked at the beer cans and broken bottles strewn across the dirty floor. My legs were tired, and my mouth was very dry, so I went to look for water. The Scot from the hostel was by the toilets smoking. He was topless, wearing just his chain, his vest hanging out his back pocket. I had lost my coat somewhere so he gave me his Puffa jacket.

'Thank you so much.'

He shook his head. 'It's no bother. I'll get you home, pal.'

Outside it was starting to get light. It had been snowing. The cold air was fresh and good. The food vans were still going. People were spilling down the stairs, smoking, their heads still moving. He bought fries and mayonnaise in cones and we ate them waiting at the cab rank, licking the hot fat and salt off our fingers. There were coloured flyers littered all over the pavement and I picked a few up and studied them.

'What you doing?' he was shivering in his vest.

'Souvenirs.' I smiled and folded them up carefully and put them in my back pocket.

In the cab I poured out the change from my purse and looked at the unfamiliar coins. 'I've not much money.'

'No bother. I've got it.' He was sat in the front chewing gum.

I wrapped myself up in his huge padded jacket and leant my head against the cold of the window. I looked at the city turned white, it was glistening. The snow softened all the hard lines.

When we got out the cab, I didn't recognise it.

'Where are we?'

'Come back to mine for a bit, for a beer?'

'Okay.'

His jaw was going as he fumbled with the keys for his flat. The door was jammed, and he needed to kick it to get it open. Inside it was one long open room, a small kitchen at one end and a bed and chair heaped with clothes at the other. In the middle was a table with two decks, long speakers either side and piles of records. There were dirty plates caked in food on the floor. There was no sofa and nothing on the walls. A thin silk sheet was pinned up covering the bottom of the window that looked out onto the street. It smelt damp. He opened the window a crack at the top and I felt the cold air stream in. I sat down on the floor with my back to the radiator whilst he flipped through his records. The music from the club was still ringing in my ears. I thought about Leah, if she was asleep back at the hostel yet, if the Italian was with her.

He put on house music and started moving his head to the beat, jutting his chin out as he opened the fridge. The sound was distorted compared to the club. I watched him as he picked up the plates from the floor and stacked them in the sink. His arms were thick and muscular. He turned to look at me.

'Beer?'

'Have you got tea?'

'Aye, but no milk.'

'Sugar?'

He nodded and swigged from his beer. I pulled my cigarettes out my back pocket and lit one. My jeans were filthy from the club, like I'd been wading in mud. I picked at the dirt and looked at the flecks settle on the laminate floor. The kettle boiled and I watched him as he searched his cupboards for a mug, then a teaspoon, then a packet of sugar. Eventually he handed me the tea, and I held it up to my mouth and blew, watching the ripples of light across the dark surface. I pulled the hood up on the Puffa, wrapped it round me and closed my eyes. I thought about sleeping. My mind felt scrambled. My skin felt sticky from the club. I wrapped my arms around my knees and when I looked up the Scot was watching me. He had taken his boots off. He turned the music up and then came to sit next to me, his back flinching against the radiator.

'You have a good one?'

I nodded.

'Where's your mate?'

I cleared my throat. 'Not sure. Back at the hostel I guess.'

'You're here for a wild weekend?' He grinned.

'We got cheap flights. I've never been here before.'

He shut his eyes, frowning, and started nodding to the music. I didn't know if he'd heard me. He looked like he was thinking, like he was about to say something serious. Then he opened his eyes and reached over for my hand and held it. His skin was rough. His nails bitten right down. He traced the lines on my palm. I looked at the ridges in his knuckles, the freckly splodges on his skin. He moved nearer and then pulled my hand and cupped it over the bulge at the top of his jeans. 'This alright?' he said but his eyes were closed. I watched my hand, unable to speak. He held it there. I could feel the heat coming off him. I looked out across the room from under my hood like I was in a tunnel. I thought about how I was here, alone, and this was happening to me. My legs felt heavy. I could see a pile of magazines under his chair. Flashes of limbs, open legs, huge breasts. I looked down at the dimpled flesh on his arms and thought about the bodies in the club, writhing. I thought about how we are all just animals in the end. I felt tired. I rested my head against his shoulder, and we stayed like that for a while, my arm draped over his leg, very still. Eventually the record finished, and the needle started to jump. He pulled himself up, so he was standing in front of me. Then he undid his belt, the metal clanking, pulled off his jeans and tossed them on the floor. His pale legs were covered in dark, wispy hair. I looked at his thighs and at the puddle of denim at my feet. He just stood there, waiting. I turned and picked up my mug and took a swig of sweet tea. I felt a pain in the front of my head. I pressed the bone around my eyes and then from under the hood I watched as his legs shuffled back over to his decks, where he put on another tune and turned the music right up.

'Mr Fingers,' he said, 'classic' and he pointed at the ceiling and sang along, 'can you feel it?' Then in his boxers and dirty white socks he started dancing. He was swivelling his hips, his hands moving like he was playing the drums. He pulled off his vest and threw it over his head onto the bed and, when he lifted his arms in the air, I could smell the sweat on him.

'Yes,' he said as the music reached a crescendo, 'yes! Tune!' He held out his hands for me to take them and started moving back towards me, 'Come on, come here.'

I didn't move, I just looked at him, at the blue veins on his arms, and then at the milky white sky out the window behind him. The sheet shifted slightly in the breeze. The music kept pulsing, his hips swaying. I looked at the shaft of light coming in from under his door, and at the speaker and the swirl of tiny holes where the sound came out. Then I reached up for him, for his hands, and he took mine and kissed the tops, like I was a queen. I let him pull me to my feet. I pulled down my hood, unzipped the jacket and let it fall to the floor.

'I'm sorry.'

'What for, pal? You're alright. Come here.' He put his hands on my hips.

'I want...'

'I know, I know, it's all good.' His face was almost touching mine, I could smell the stale gum on his breath. I looked down at his socks, and then at the tip of his tongue as he ran it over his teeth. He touched my hair, then cheek, then went to kiss me, but I pulled back.

'I want to go.'

'You what?'

'Sorry. See you tomorrow?'

Then I kissed his sweaty cheek and walked out the door.

Outside, I crossed over. I could hear him calling after me, but I ran, his music fading into the distance, my skin prickling in the cold. I breathed deeply, blowing out air like smoke, my feet crunching, making fresh marks in the snow. The road was empty, all noise hushed, and black skeletal trees lined the pavements, their bone-like branches rising up. I stopped to catch my breath and scored a line in the snow on the top of a parked car with my finger, feeling the sting of the cold, then stuck the crystals in my mouth and let them dissolve. Tall terracotta buildings lined the street, one after the other, small slotted windows, little squares of light, and I thought about the people inside, their bodies warm, sleeping. At the crossing the odd car started to appear, moving slowly, their engines muffled. I turned down the main stretch to look for a cab and saw a flash of movement. Red fur against the white. It skirted along the street then jumped and poked its nose into a skip, its dirty stomach stretched over the metal rim. I walked into the grey slush of the road to get a better look. Its tongue was out, and it was gnawing at a bone. I took another step towards it, but it looked up at me with its pale green eyes and I froze, suddenly frightened it might bite.

Inside the hostel they were laying out the breakfast buffet - cereals and yoghurt, bowls of fruit, rye bread, cold meats and cheese on slates. I poured myself a cup of hot coffee and climbed the stairs, feeling the pull in the muscles at the bottom of my legs. I opened the door carefully, nervous the Italian might be there, but it was just Leah, mouth open, fast asleep. Her make-up was smudged, and she was holding her pillow. I grabbed my towel, went to the showers and stood under the hot water feeling it beat against my neck, watching the soapy water run down me, letting the room fill up with steam.

In bed, the cotton duvet was soft and fresh. I lay wide awake, listening to the wheeze of Leah's breathing. I looked up at the ceiling and the tiny red light flashing on the fire alarm in the corner. I thought about my body shining in the lights of the club, and the feeling of his thick, rough hands. I turned over and pressed my hand hard between my legs and rocked quickly until I came. Then I closed my eyes, and thought about the days we had left, and what else I would do.

Note: The story was within the 3,000-word limit when selected; this is a slightly longer final draft.

I KNEW YOU THEN
Kelly Kirwan

"What are you writing?" Ray leans over, hand on my thigh, chin resting on my shoulder. Everything about Ray is slinky, suggestive. He grins in slow half-smiles, punctuates conversations with light touches.

We've fallen into this staged sort of flirtation recently. Affection as a joke.

I close my notebook, hiding the list on the page. "Homework."

He nods, pulls an orange out of his lunch bag.

"I hung out with Julie last night," he offers, scanning the cafeteria. I watch his fingers dig into the rind, the mist of citrus, the peel curling until it skims the top of the table. He pops a slice into his mouth. Saliva pools on my tongue.

Ray swallows. "Took her top off—huge tits."

He hands me a slice, which I take carefully, pulling off the white threads, the veins of the fruit.

I turn to him solemnly. "You're disgusting."

"I know, I know. *A pig.*" He beams, amused by my disapproval.

I laugh, a cheap one, studying his carelessness. How he slips into situations loose-limbed, noncommittal.

He glances over, "What?"

"Nothing."

"No. What are you thinking?"

"What Julie's cup size is."

He bumps me lightly, "And I thought you were turning into such a prude."

My smile fades, a sting spreading like a welt. *Turning into.*

"Casey, a prude?"

Ray and I turn, surprised by the interruption. Our table's circular, an eight-seater, and most days our conversations remain separate—Ray and I, the rest of the table. From the outside it would be hard to see the split. We still seem unified, a group tinged with a certain recklessness. The first to drink, to smoke, to do more than kiss—sending ripples across social circles and then setting a new boundary.

But Ray and I had crossed a line. Separately, but to the same effect. A piecemeal isolation, waiting on the disdain of our friends to either thaw or make way for larger judgment.

I'd never asked Ray what happened. I'd heard scattered pieces, something impulsive, stupid, vaguely criminal. *Stealing.*

For me, it had been the cardinal sin of ruined reputation. Too slutty, too drunk.

"I think we all know by now not to leave Casey alone, drunk, with a boy," Erin says benignly, braiding her hair out of boredom. The table shifts uncomfortably.

I feel a deep blush in my cheeks, a radiating burgundy heat. I give a near imperceptible shrug, a mild gesture I realize too late seems like an agreement.

Erin runs a hand over the crown of her head, checking for rogue strands. The chatter of the cafeteria blurs into a fog, all-consuming.

Someone, I'm not sure who, makes a bland observation and the tension breaks.

Ray gives a flimsy smile, resetting. "What are you doing to that poor orange?"

I'd torn the slice in half, distracted, juice sticky on my fingers. I pop it into my mouth, the citrus sweet and acidic. Overwhelming.

The bell rings in a sharp, siren-like pitch, and the cafeteria shifts into a new chaos. Ray stretches, shirt lifting to show his belly button stretched taut over muscle. "Walk with me?"

I shake my head. "Go ahead. I'll see you in English."

He slings his backpack over his shoulder, joining the shuffle toward the exit. I flip to the back page of my notebook, add *orange slice* to the list.

When I look up the cafeteria is empty, giving an eerie sense of skewed time. That I could have been alone for minutes or hours—impossible to tell.

***

The Ceramics Room has rectangular tables jutting out at odd angles, maze-like. It's a room of tchotchkes, mismatched tupperware filled with paint brushes, a mausoleum of broken projects lining the windowsill.

Upperclassmen sit at the center table, letting younger grades eavesdrop on our conversations, the drama, the believed maturity of it. Today though, John and Deanna keep their voices low, discreet exchanges I fade in and out of. I had left my project partially exposed overnight, the clay now cracked, rigid in my fist.

John sits at the head of the table, our subversive golden boy: honor student, varsity soccer player, artwork displayed in the glass cabinet in our school's foyer.

"Would Ray really do that, though?" Deanna asks, her voice sandpapery. The side effect of an aggressive smoking habit.

I look up.

"He did do it," John says firmly, carving his clay with a razor blade.

Deanna watches his movements, almost meditative. "How do you know?"

"He knows the code to my house. He watched me put the money in my drawer the day before." John lists the facts, curving the blade with a preternatural calmness, "He was out sick the same day it went missing. Now suddenly he has all this new shit."

Deanna raises her eyebrows, impassive. She's blunt, practical, disinterested in stoking drama. I've always liked her. She sighs. "So, what're you going to do?"

"I don't know. He's such an asshole. I'd have a lot more respect for him if he just admitted it."

"Did you tell your parents?"

"No," he says, offended: *snitch*. "It's between us."

John notices me then, my silent participation, the misshapen lump of clay in my hand. "What's that supposed to be, Casey?" he says, not meanly.

I hold up my project, notice the clay caked beneath my fingernails. "Um. Abstract?"

Deanna laughs, a boom that jolts the younger kids sitting near us. John's mouth twitches, eyes steely. He starts packing up his project, painstakingly tucking the plastic sheet around his tray.

"Ray's always been a scumbag," he says, thinking out loud. "Always takes it too far."

"You were friends, though," I say, an obvious statement. Half a question.

John tosses the blade into a tupperware on the table, filled with other tools: wires, scalpel-looking objects. Ordinary things that could turn predatory if grabbed at the wrong angle, a thoughtless clutch.

He stares at me blankly, "Not anymore."

***

English.

We're on our second day of watching a movie, a sluggish documentary on blacklists in the '50s, the looming threat of commies. Ms. Silva rewinds to our place from yesterday, images flitting on the screen in rapid reverse.

Ray walks in with two cupcakes from his last class, leftovers from some celebration.

"Casey, look, cupcakes," he says happily, a half-ironic, kid-like giddiness.

He places one on my desk, a tiny thing you would find in a plastic twelve pack at the grocery store. I unwrap the paper methodically, place a minuscule drop of icing on my tongue.

"How slow do you eat?" Ray asks, mouth full. The smell of confectioner's sugar swirls in my nostrils. I feel a pang in my side, like a stitch.

I take a bite, feeling cornered. I start tracing words on my desk, an automatic tic—coffee, orange slice, cupcake—in invisible cursive.

"What's this?" Ray whispers, mimicking my fingers.

I stop, "Nothing."

He tilts his head, "You're pretty weird, you know that?"

"I've noticed, yeah."

"Well, I like that you're a big old freak."

I laugh, relaxing into my seat. Ray grins, pleased with himself. There's an easiness to our interactions, the lulls in our conversations. A relief in insulation.

I hear myself asking before I'd even fully decided.

"Did you steal that money from John?"

Instantly, I regret it.

Ray tenses, the air between us changing. "Why are you asking me that?"

I falter, "He thinks you did."

"You were talking about me?"

"No, he brought it up. Not even to me, I was just there."

"When?"

"Today. In Ceramics."

"What else did he say?"

I open my mouth, empty of a right answer.

"Fuck, Casey, what did he say?"

"Nothing," I hiss, glancing at the rest of the room.

Ray leans forward, something in him aggressive, unpredictable.

"Do you think I took it?"

"Did you?"

"No," he says finally, a sheen of disgust. "I didn't."

He faces forward, fixating on the TV screen.

I stand, chair scraping the floor, grabbing the hall pass from its nearby perch.

Everything in the girl's bathroom is pink. Pepto-Bismol colored walls, a magenta, tangy-smelling soap. It's empty, so I fling open the door to the closest stall, knees bent in front of the toilet. I stretch my finger to the back of my throat, feel the scratch, the lurch, spit a putrid yellow bile into the water. The toilet's automatic and it starts to flush, over and over, as if possessed. I jump, not expecting it, then break into a volatile fit of laughter, drowned out by the sound of water relentlessly circling the drain.

Ray glances at me when I walk back into class. I'm hyper-aware of my movements, sitting beside him without turning, stretching my arms so my fingers grip the edge of the desk. He edges closer, gently reaching out his hand. I watch as he gently strokes the knuckle of my middle finger. I hadn't seen: the skin ripped at the joint, a small cut from grating teeth, lightly bleeding.

***

The tennis courts are wedged between the track and soccer field, surrounded by hedges and hidden from outside view. My gym clothes are baggy, stale, stuffed into a locker for too long. I walk to the farthest court, the most isolated, picking up a tennis ball from the crate. A shadow stretches over me.

"Partner?"

Ray's voice is light, kind. We're always partners. It's an apology, or an offer to forget. I shrug, toss him the ball and walk to the far side of the net. He looks hurt, maybe annoyed. It's unsettling that I can't tell the difference.

We volley with tight, aggressive swings. Beads of sweat collect on my back, trail down my chest. Ray's sneakers skid, reaching a ball just barely in-bounds. He swings his racket with a low, guttural grunt, and I sprint to the right side of the court. I used to be lightning fast, the lynchpin in every relay. But now the blood rushes from my temples, flickers of light speckling my vision.

I blink and one hand is on the ground, digging into grainy concrete.

Ray rushes over, "You OK?"

"Just light-headed," I answer, voice breathy.

"Should I get Coach Allen?"

"No." It's firm. I close my mouth, inhale deeply, feel the fuzziness start to fade.

Ray sits next to me, patient.

I rest my cheek on my knee to face him.

He mirrors me. "You look better."

"I doubt it."

"You do. Such a beauty."

"You say that to all the girls."

"Not really."

I raise my eyebrows, smile carefully. Trying to find the joke.

He stands, offers his hand to pull me up, grabs my other arm to steady me. He has that crisp smell of mint, like one of those deodorants that would be named *Alpine Blue* or *Cool Ice*. It's subtle, how he pulls me in, my head resting on his chest. An intimacy that's unlike me. We stand like this for a few minutes, completely still.

Then softly he says, "Be careful, OK?"

I imagine asking him what he means, deflecting. But I'm too tired.

So instead I say, "You too."

***

There's a dance tonight.

We're sitting on the plush carpet of Erin's room, walls still pale yellow from when she was eight, hand-painted butterflies flying up from the corner. I remember the day it was finished.

It's a ritual before dances to steal alcohol from our parents, water bottles filled with different colored liquors in the center of our circle.

"Casey," Erin says, wincing after a shot, "Tell us about Ray."

All the girls turn except Deanna, who studies Erin warily. Unamused.

"What do you mean?"

Erin rolls her eyes, "You guys are all over each other."

"We're just friends," I say, sipping a sugary iced tea, rinsing away the lingering taste of vodka.

"I think he likes you." Deanna says casually, puncturing a small hole in whatever case was being built.

Erin ignores her. "You haven't hooked up?" She asks, stretching out her legs, blue dress hiked up to her thighs.

"No." It's a knee-jerk answer, the suddenness of it sounding guilty. "He'd flirt with anyone."

Erin considers this, grinning slowly. "You're right. He would."

Her smile is devious, ugly, knowing. I memorize it, the curl of her lips, suddenly outraged by the childishness of her room. Once sweet but now out of place, curdled by time.

It's disorienting being in school at night. In the darkened gym, with blaring pop-synth hits, I feel drunk. My limbs are lead-heavy, reactions delayed. We're with the boys in the corner, always referencing them in this way: the boys. As in, *will the boys be there?*

My phone buzzes in my purse.

A text from Ray, *Here?*

Yeah where are you? I type back, feeling myself grin.

Deanna tilts her hand, miming a drink. She smuggled a flask in her purse, ripping the lining for a makeshift false bottom. Erin nods, a few of the girls following, arms slung around each other's necks to cross the dance floor in swaying strides.

When they leave John comes over to me, leaning in so I can hear him. "Have you seen Ray?"

"No," I shout, strained over the music.

He looks at me skeptically, cheek brushing mine, "You shouldn't hang out with him."

"No?"

He shakes his head, breath on my neck, "He always said how easy you were. How you two were gonna fuck."

The song overhead rings in my ears, a kick-drum building into a deafening crescendo.

"I told him you were a nice girl," John says, as if this were sanctimonious, "I just thought you should know."

I go out the side doors of the gym, heading toward the bathrooms at the end of the senior hall. Less busy than the ones near the entrance. I've become good at siphoning time, filling my day with detours. At night, the school keeps on every other light in the hall, alternating between a green-yellow glow and stretches of darkness. Spooky.

I round a corner and stop-short at the sight of two bodies, tangled in one another against the lockers. A mouth on the neck, hand on the thigh.

"Sorry," I say automatically, as they pull away from each other, my hand flying up as a small curtain of privacy. Then I catch it: the familiarity of her dress, his shoes.

Ray's standing with his arms at his sides, now an arm's length away from Erin. She's smoothing the fabric of her dress with a forced concentration, unable to look up. When she does she can't hold it. For the first time in months I feel a flicker of our old friendship.

"Sorry," I say again, all other words shapeless, foreign. I back away. "Sorry."

The air outside is muggy. Thick. I walk through the parking lot quickly, the straps of my sandals digging into my ankles. Ray catches up, grabbing my arm so I skid-stop, alcohol sloshing in my stomach. I whip my arm away as he releases it, nearly falling from my own momentum.

"Are you OK?"

"Fine, yeah. I just needed air," I say roughly, starting to second-guess his question.

"You seem upset," he says quietly.

"I think I drank too much."

"Can I get you anything?"

"No, you should go back inside. Erin's probably waiting." My words are lilting, synthetic.

"She…" He gives up. "Isn't."

Another pause.

"John's looking for you," I say casually, feeling vengeful.

There's a flicker of concern, but he doesn't move.

We're surrounded by the static of electrical wires, the buzz of cicadas; white noise that feels prickly on my skin.

I know the answer but need to ask again. "Did you take the money?"

Ray barely reacts. Just exhales. "Yeah."

That's it. No seismic shift.

"Why?"

"I don't know. I didn't plan it. I just—felt like it." Each word is sharper, more frustrated. "Why'd you fuck Dave Hall when he had a girlfriend?"

"That's not what happened."

"He says it did."

My voice sounds warbled, palms slick with sweat.

"He said he blacked out."

"Yeah, I think he said *what a waste.*"

It's a gut-punch, paralytic. Ray sees it too, the wound.

Dave Hall, an ace 3-point shooter, whose name is the favored chant at basketball games. Who had a girlfriend but said, *let me help you,* when I fell asleep on the couch. The day after was vivid, sunny to the point of surreal. Outwardly unchanged. But I could feel it even then, a poison spreading, inverting my worldview.

I turn to leave. Ray doesn't follow.

I'm relieved that I don't want him to.

⚹

I hear about it first-thing on Monday, along with everyone else.

Events like this always become common knowledge, turning to myth with passing embellishments.

It must have happened right after I left.

Ray sees me in the hall, hesitates. As he comes over I see the deep purple bruise under his eye, his split lip.

He has the air of being unfazed.

"Good weekend?"

"Sure."

He nods repeatedly, mustering the words. "Look, I'm sorry. For what I said. I don't care about what happened with Dave Hall." He's hasty, sincere. "I mean, think of all the times I've fucked up," he adds, offering a laugh that dies quickly.

It's then I realize, our mistake.

We both thought we were the same.

Ray still believed it.

I'd always thought of the truth as being complex, layered, redeeming. I never imagined that it could be a dead end. Curt and senseless. As simple as: because someone felt like it.

I study the scab on my knuckle, shriveled and healing. The bell rings for first period. Ray looks at me, expectant. And I wonder what we are to each other, underneath: a distraction or a need.

THE BASKET AND THE FLASK
Jean Roarty

My friendship with Siobhan Rigney was cemented forever in first class. We had both been picked to collect the nuns' lunches daily from the nearby convent. We were seven years old. Of course we didn't let on we were pleased or Mother Fahy would have put a stop to it.

Escaping her violence for a while each day was heaven.

My other job meant missing some class time as well. Every morning I had to get a massive jug of ink from the office and fill the inkwells.

'Doesn't matter if your raggy clothes get stained, Molloy,' Mother Fahy had said.

To the outside world she epitomised kindness and compassion. To those who knew her, her mission was to cause pain. Mostly she sat away from us at her desk. In the drawer she had a half-inch-thick ruler, along with a tin of stale biscuits. At other times she patrolled the classroom in her long, black habit, her callous face encircled, daisy-like, in a wimple. An oversized rosary dangled from her waist. Her rasping voice terrorised us. She smelt of chalk and mothballs. Up and down, up and down she prowled, ruler in hand. Her ominous footsteps would stop, then for no reason, without warning, one of us would get belted.

I felt guilty for being glad when it wasn't me.

Behind Mother Fahy's desk was the blackboard and chalk. The week before Christmas, the wooden duster, which she often used as a missile, had blinded Colette McNamara in her right eye. Above the blackboard on the wall hung a crucifix. Another free-standing crucifix stood on her desk. It had a wooden base, like steps. When Mother Fahy used it as a weapon, the steely bit pierced our skin. A large square, brown bin sat in the corner. Most days one of us had to stand in the bin until we fainted. We never knew why. It was for things like not looking pious enough during prayers. We also had to kneel for hours in front of the statue of Our Lady in the yard, in the rain. I knew every inch of that statue: the blue shawl falling in folds, speckled with bird dirt; the bare foot that peeped out from the white dress; the way the paint on the foot was chipped as if a toenail was missing.

'I told everyone to come in with their hair tied back,' Mother Fahy said one morning after roll call. She glared at Kathleen O'Brien who sat directly in front of me. Kathleen's wavy black hair cascaded down her back.

'I couldn't find a rubber band,' said Kathleen, whose mother was sick. No one in our row had bobbins or ribbons.

'I'll teach you not to have a rubber band.'

Mother Fahy took the twine out of her desk drawer, cut a piece and tied Kathleen's long hair in a ponytail. Then she got her scissors, grabbed hold of the ponytail and sliced it off. A collective gasp went around the room. All day the black hair, like a dog's tail, lay in the bin, sunk backwards on its own curls.

Kathleen's mother died two days later.

The daily escape to the convent kept me and Siobhan going. To the envy of the rest of the class, we left every day after the Angelus. We charged into the bright light of the yard and tore down the lane to the road that led to St Brigid's convent. Our school, St Brigid's National School, was the only primary school in the Clooneen area.

Filled with joyous freedom, Siobhan and I would carry out our mission. As soon as we'd collected the wicker basket we'd peep under the tea towel. The sight of cheese and apples—food we could only dream of—deepened our hunger pains.

Each day we took turns carrying either the basket or flask, returning as the lunch bell sounded. Mother Fahy had warned us to be back on time and not to break the flask. We feared what she might do if we messed up. The day Siobhan broke the May-altar vase, Mother Fahy had slammed her head against the wall.

There were four rows of wooden desks. The row nearest the windows, where Siobhan and I sat, was the Dunces' Row. It was for poor girls with little parental backup— girls used to hardship. As well as the inevitable cruel, mental torment and beatings, Mother Fahy would bang the desk tops down on our forearms at every opportunity. We knew the answers to sums and spellings ages before anyone in the other rows; we also knew not to put our hands up.

Siobhan and I lived from moment to moment. We'd say 'Thanks be to God' the minute we got as far as the yard. Then we'd laugh and joke our way up and down to the convent.

'Knock, knock,' Siobhan would say.

'Who's there?'

'Nun.'

'Nun who?'

'None of your business.'

Then I'd take a turn. We'd keep it going for ages.

One day just as we arrived back to the yard, Siobhan dropped the flask on the hard concrete. Fright crept up me. She picked it up and shook it. I watched her fingers tremble as she unscrewed the top and looked in.

It was still intact.

I hugged her.

'Careful,' she said, holding the flask tighter than ever.

Another day, not long after, we decided to explore, but got lost. Luckily, we heard the school bell and raced towards it. We were later than normal with the lunches. With one hand clutching the handle of the basket, I knocked on the staffroom door. After a long, silent pause, we heard the squeaking of a chair. Mother Fahy opened the door. To our astonishment, she took the lunches without a word. From then on we were more careful about the amount of time we spent climbing trees and daring each other into the nuns' graveyard. We often sneaked in behind the thorny hedge to gaze in awe at the uniform lines of headstones. In the graveyard we knelt on the dewy grass, blessed ourselves and prayed: *Please God let our teacher die. Amen.*

After handing in the nuns' lunches, we drank from the water fountain and ate what we had. Neither of us ever had much. Siobhan had four brothers and five sisters. They lived in the council houses. My father had been killed when I was four. Mammy didn't even have a penny when I needed it, to buy a pencil. Because Daddy had died on the roadside without a priest, Mother Fahy said he'd burn in Hell for all eternity.

One day I coughed during prayers.

'How dare you insult God, Molloy,' roared Mother Fahy. She grabbed the ruler and headed for me. Pain shot through my head as blow after blow rained down. I tried to pull away, tried to shield my head with my hands. When she finally stopped, blood was trickling from my left ear. I smeared it away, feeling the damp stickiness in my hair and on my face. Afterwards, during reading, my head felt strange. I looked at my book. The letters kept moving around. When it was my turn to read, I said 'The words are on top of each other.'

Mother Fahy took a Marietta biscuit from her tin and came over to me.

'Don't tell anyone, Margaret,' she said, placing the biscuit on top of my book. I wasn't sure if she was referring to the biscuit or the blood. That was the first kindness she had ever shown me. The biscuit tasted soft and smelt of paint. She had never called me by my first name before, only ever using words like *stupid brat*. Mother Fahy moved her hand to inspect the blood that dribbled from my ear. I flinched. My head ached. A sense of grievance bubbled up inside me.

If Mammy had been at home after school I would have told her, but every day we let ourselves in the window to an empty flat. Mammy was out doing any work she could get. Daddy had died destitute. He didn't leave a pension. There was no widow's pension or social welfare. Married women couldn't work.

It was probably just as well Mammy was never at home. After Mother Fahy had broken Mary's arm dragging her out of her desk, Mary's mother found out. For the rest of the term Mother Fahy beat Mary even more, saying 'That'll teach you to go running home, telling tales.'

For the next few days Mother Fahy picked on the others more than me. Each day was still fraught; horror seeped into me as I witnessed her cruelty. I counted the days until the summer holidays.

One morning towards the end of June, Mother Fahy made an announcement.

'We'll be finishing up for the summer soon.'

I glanced at Siobhan. Our eyes met. We were afraid to smile.

'When you return in September, you will be in second class.' Then the devastating blow. 'I will be taking you again next year.'

'Oh no,' slipped out of my mouth. Luckily Mother Fahy didn't hear.

After the Angelus we set off to the convent as usual. The wind pasted our dresses to our legs as we walked. The prospect of another year with Mother Fahy weighed on us. On our way back Siobhan found a discarded apple core on the pavement. She had just picked it up to finish it, when a brown terrier with a white ear ran towards us and whipped to a stop. It stared at us. I could see its eyes. I wanted to stroke it, but had the flask in my hands. Next thing the dog stiffened. The hairs bristled on the back of its neck. It started growling and nipping at our heels. We screamed.

I dropped the flask.

Siobhan dropped the basket.

We jumped up on to the nearest garden wall. From there we could see the dog foraging around in the basket. Apples spiralled in different directions. We watched the flask ricochet off the footpath and roll down the road making a scratchy noise. There was no one in sight.

Siobhan and I stood on the wall, fear jabbing our stomachs.

'Stop, doggie,' I shouted, but to no avail.

Finally the dog bounded off. Panic filled Siobhan's eyes. At that moment we feared the dog returning more than we feared Mother Fahy.

'Now's our chance,' said Siobhan. We leapt off the wall and raced back empty-handed to the school, not stopping until we had reached the main door. We sank down on the concrete steps, panting.

Confusion and fear pounded in my head, giving me a dizzy feeling.

'She'll kill us,' I said. 'We'd better go back and get what's left.'

'What about the dog?' Siobhan raised her voice above the sound of the bell.

A familiar fear stirred within me. Siobhan started to cry. The sound of the bell awoke something in me. I would go in and face Mother Fahy. And I would go alone.

'You go back to the classroom Siobhan. I'll tell her what happened. I'll be fine—the other teachers will be there.'

Siobhan hugged me before heading off, turning around to give me a last glance.

Walking down the dark corridor, I began to have second thoughts. I should have made Siobhan come with me. My determination gave way to fear. I forced myself to knock on the staffroom door. Mother Fahy opened it immediately.

'A dog ate the lunches,' I blurted out.

Mother Fahy glared at me.

'What did ye do with them?'

'Nothing.'

'Nothing?'

I looked her in the eye. 'The dog ate them.'

'You lying brat.'

I stood tall and caught a glimpse of the other teachers in the staffroom staring down at their lunches. I looked back up into Mother Fahy's eyes and said 'I am not. I never tell lies.'

Before I knew it, Mother Fahy had grabbed my wrist and was pulling me down the corridor. With her other hand, she snatched the window pole that lay propped against the wall. She yanked me out the main door, the fine black cloth of her habit billowing about her ankles.

The yard was deserted. Everyone was inside eating their lunches. Mother Fahy stopped suddenly. I jerked forwards. She raised the pole to strike me. I wrenched my wrist free and darted behind the statue of Our Lady. Mother Fahy loomed large at the far side, like a giant magpie.

For a fleeting moment I thought this is like a game of peek-a-boo.

'Help me,' I prayed, touching Our Lady's back.

The heavens rumbled. Big drops of rain struck the statue like bullets. Mother Fahy lunged towards me with the pole. I tensed waiting for the blow. She slipped on the wet ground. Her head struck Our Lady's protruding foot. She lay on the ground like a black paper plane, the side of her wimple stained Ribena-red.

Until that moment I didn't know she had blood in her veins.

Two Poems
Kęstutis Navakas

98.

no one can find immaneul kant
anywhere. he was never there. manu-
factured by krupp factories his tongue

is steel. after that he was purchased
by some colorful countries full of
strange butterflies. immanuel kant

does not exist like the tea we drink
and the air we breathe and the water
through which we paddle along and

the words we would speak this morning

Translation by Rimas Uzgiris of Kęstutis Navakas' "devyniasdešimt aštuntas" from 100 du *(Vilnius: Apostrofa, 2013)*

PEOPLE

strange people are walking through my rooms
they came from countries whose names have not
yet been coined. cartography does not apply to them
and ptolemy returns to take a rest on three elephants.
these people don't speak. after every colon in
the text a blank space is left. the people move
my furniture around according to a system of their own
and it seems they don't even understand what furniture is
strange that there are people who don't understand something
they came they're here they even brought clothes they...
and who knows what will happen if nobody calls
i'll be left with these people i'm beginning to understand
they are i. all of them are my self and stem. in other
words – all of me is them. other. crossed out. expired.

Translation by Rimas Uzgiris of Kęstutis Navakas' "žmonės"

WHO DO WE WANT TO BE?
Theo Dorgan

Note: In 2019, together with Philip King, Gary Hynes and Mark Patrick Hederman, Theo Dorgan was invited to make a presentation to the Oireachtas Joint Committee on Arts, Heritage and the Gaeltacht. The following text was submitted to the Committee in advance, at their request, to facilitate a better understanding of the author's argument. The verbal presentation, together with the submissions made by the other invitees, and the discussion that followed, can be accessed through the Oireachtas TV website.

One hundred years ago the first Dáil met to consider one simple and profound question: who do we want to be?

The question had first been posed, and answered, in the Proclamation of 1916, the answer implicit in the promise that the new Republic would cherish the children of the nation.

Even as the Dáil was meeting, the Irish and British newspapers, the bankers, the civil servants and that whole floating population of people who think themselves sophisticated and in the know were sneering at the absurdity of it all. How unrealistic, they thought and said, a handful of people, known to nobody who mattered, having the temerity to set up a comic opera parliament with pretensions to rule over Ireland. This was the response of the people, still with us, who know, as Wilde put it, the price of everything and the value of nothing.

There you have it in miniature, at the birth of our independent State, the perpetual conflict between so-called realism and the imagination.

The fact is, the Rising was an act of imagination, a handful of ill-armed amateur soldiers up against a huge military machine, a sophisticated and wealthy Empire, a skilled and infinitely capable political apparatus of government. And yet, those amateurs set in train the fall of the greatest empire the world had known until then.

It is not irrelevant that three of the seven signatories were poets, that James Connolly was a talented songwriter. It is not irrelevant that the 30 years leading up to the Rising was a period of enormous cultural and artistic ferment. The Republic we now enjoy was, and still is, a product of liberated imagination. We imagined our liberty, our independence, we had the courage to imagine ourselves free and self-determined, and we made it come to pass.

Just so, the first Dáil imagined itself as the parliament of a free Ireland, and it came to pass.

Never, ever, underestimate the power of imagination.

Everything begins in the imagination. There was a moment when each member of this Committee imagined herself or himself as a Deputy to the Dáil—and I'm sure that some of you imagine yourselves as Ministers, perhaps even as Taoiseach. Imagining ourselves forward in our lives is what we do, it is the primary instrument by which we grow as human beings, as a society.

The primary question we face now in Ireland is, who do we want to be? We are many, and various, and becoming more various and capable by the year. We are a privileged country in the context of a world in turmoil, a world of upheaval and poverty. We are a stable society, a democracy with a developed civil and civic apparatus, a proper separation of powers between executive and judiciary, an obedient army firmly under the control of parliament, a relatively stable economy—we enjoy a cautious good fortune. But we have to ask ourselves, is this all we are? Does this sum us up? Is this what so many women and so many men have struggled for in the past 100 years?

The answer, of course, is no, or a qualified no. All of this is good, and worthy, and not to be undervalued. But, is it enough to explain us? To ourselves and to the world? What will we have contributed to the world, to civilisation?

It helps, sometimes, to look back through the mists of history and see what stands clear. I had the deeply embarrassing experience of being in Greece some years ago when the then Minister for Finance asked, "What did Greece ever give us only feta cheese?" (For the record, he was to some extent quoted out of context). For day after day, on the hourly news bulletins, the Minister was shown against a backdrop of three young people huddled in sleeping bags on the Ha'penny Bridge. I only wish that Greek television and newspapers had given equal space to the witty letter published in *The Irish Times* the day after the Minister's remark: "Ah yes, what did Greece ever give us except philosophy, theology, geology, geography, theatre, poetry... and democracy."

The enduring legacy of Classical Greece is still with us, but we need to remember, as a matter of urgency, that we have this legacy because of the still relevant drama of Euripides, Sophocles, Aeschylus, the poems of Sappho and Homer, the statues and buildings of the myriad masters, the writings of Plato and Aristotle.

The glory that was Greece was established not just by wise rulers like Solon, not just by the wise councils of Athens, but through the power of its artists' imaginations, and even more so by the integration of art and statecraft, the ever-present dialogue, and indeed productive tension, between both.

We remember Greece, and how Greece shaped the European mind, so let me ask, for what will Ireland be remembered in the coming times? What is it we do, now, here, that has the admiration of the world, that shows us as a proud, humane and distinctive people?

Well, of course you all know, but let me offer you a list at random: Joyce, Yeats, Beckett, Heaney, Shaw—and let me add some names from among the living: Eavan Boland, John Banville, Anne Enright, Colm Tóibín, Edna O'Brien, Roddy Doyle, Nuala Ní Dhomhnaill, Sinéad O'Connor, Martin Hayes, Iarla Ó Lionáird. U2... And now let me add, at random almost, Druid in Theatre, Neil Jordan, Lenny Abrahamson, Liam Neeson and Saoirse Ronan in film, Seán Scully in painting... world figures all. Well, good, it's nice to be able to list off the names of powerful women and men of achievement. But it can be misleading, this cataloguing of 'world-class' individuals. The focus on great individual achievement can serve to mask and obscure the depth and breadth of the culture out of which these individuals emerge. The English physicist Sir Isaac Newton said, and he meant it, "If I have seen further than other men, it is because I have stood on the shoulders of giants."

As in physics, so in art: it is not our business to dwell absentmindedly on the great, to bask complacently in the light they shed, as if their achievements had anything to do with us. Our business, if I might reach from culture to agriculture for a metaphor, is to cultivate the forest, to nourish the local talent and be proud of it, to train up and support the foresters, to enrich the soil out of which the giants can reach towards the sun.

Fanciful? Not a bit of it. There is not a street or a housing estate in Ireland, not a rural parish or a small town, that does not have in it children learning instruments, somebody painting, somebody writing, someone passionate about theatre, film, traditional music, popular or classical music—and very often, too, one of the living masters of an art form. Who we are will be shaped and determined by what we do for these people, how we provide for the full flowering of their interests and gifts. How we provide for the nourishment and care of these infinite and infinitely different imaginations. How we value them.

I ask the question again, who do we want to be? It was Pearse's question, and Connolly's, it was the question posed by the Countess Markievicz and Maud Gonne, by Joyce and Yeats—but also by Collins and de Valera, by Todd Andrews, Seán Lemass, T.K. Whittaker, by Mary Robinson and Mary McAleese, in our time posed luminously by President Higgins; it is the question posed daily by us all, and the question is qualified, quantified, complicated and enriched not just by the architects of the State but by the woman who hurries from work to send her daughter to a Comhaltas session, the man who stays in town after work to go to the Abbey or the Taibhdhearc, the child locked in her bedroom struggling to master an instrument—and it is the question posed by every man and woman who lifts their head, maybe a little puzzled, and realises that no more is being asked of them but to be an obedient, unquestioning cog in the machine, a statistic in an economist's report. Who do we want to be? Who do I want to be? How best to imagine a more fulfilling life?

The answer, often hesitant and unsure, is always: I want my life to mean something, I want to enjoy the human release of knowing there is more to life than this. And this is why we turn to our books, to our cinema screens, our galleries, our concert halls and small back rooms in pubs that shelter our music, we turn to our many arts for comfort, for questions that mean something, for a sense of something greater and more meaningful in life. We turn to these things, these places, in order to be lifted up.

This is a natural, unforced and uncomplicated response. Human beings are formed and shaped to want and need the comfort and sustenance of having our imaginations fed and challenged, stretched and enlightened. It is our nature to search out meaning and pleasure, and especially to search out the products of the imagination that offer the infinite variety of both.

Agree with me then, please, that the imagination is our primary shaping power, and let me propose to you that our artists, in all disciplines, are the engineers, the architects, the economists and the explorers of the imagination. The artist, in whatever discipline—your child, your neighbour, your neighbour's child, your niece or nephew, your best friend from school, that curious fellow who lives at the end of the road—the artist is one of us, and their gift to us is the generous and necessary work they do in cultivating, exploring and demonstrating, day in and day out, the unstoppable and exhilarating power of the imagination. It is very much to our shame that while we profit from the work of these artists, while we glory in their achievements, we are content that most of them are ruthlessly condemned to live in poverty.

So now I have a question to share with the Committee: why does the Department of Finance not understand this? Is there a special test to ensure that nobody who values and understands the imagination is allowed serve in that Department? Or is there some secret medical procedure employed to strip these particular individuals of their capacity to understand that we are building here not just a necessary economy but an indispensable civilisation?

I ask because the Department has consistently and ruthlessly clung to the notion that money spent on the arts is money down the drain. Consistently, and with a dreary predictability, they have refused to understand that money spent through, for instance, The Arts Council/An Chomhairle Ealaíon is an investment. Do they not understand the concept of investment for return?

I will offer a small example of why this is so lamentable. The Indecon Report of 2011 tells us that, of the €68 million assigned to the Council that year, €47 million came straight back into State coffers as PAYE, PRSI and VAT from organisations kept in being with the aid of Council grants. The difference is €21 million, so that represents the State's investment. The return to the economy directly attributable to the work done by those organisations, and the artists whose work they showcased and employed, was €148 million. So you give me 21 and I give you back 148—tell me, in those circumstances, would you offer me double the next year, treble?

The same Indecon report estimates the net contribution to the economy of all arts & creative industries in that year may be put at €750 million. Why is it—I have been asking myself this question for almost 40 years—why is it that we cannot or will not understand that investment in the arts, in our artists, in our collective national imagination, is precisely and exactly that, an investment? On the crudest possible level, of money for money, it is a fabulously productive investment. More than this, though, and above all else, this investment is what makes it possible for us to answer, over and over again, the only question that truly matters in any society: who do we want to be?

My own answer is as blunt and simple as the answer given by the monks of the Middle Ages who fanned out across a Europe plunged in turmoil and in darkness: we want to be a light in a world growing darker by the day.

POEMS
Maram Al-Masri

Translations by Theo Dorgan of "The Bread of Letters" and parts 3 and 34 of "The Abduction" by Maram al-Masri

THE BREAD OF LETTERS

I

Who will tell the trees they are guilty
for having let fall their leaves,
who will accuse the sea of abandoning its shells on the sand?

I, mother-woman, woman-mother,
with two breasts for pleasure
two breasts for maternity
who gives the milk of music
tells stories
explains games
clarifies feelings
and the grammar of thoughts.
I, who am woman voluptuous tender,
virtuous and sinner,
with my mouth
I give to eat the bread of letters,
consonants and vowels,
phrases, synonyms and comparisons.

Who will accuse me,
I who make a gift of my body
to love?

2

The act of writing,
is it not a scandalous act in itself?

To write,
it is learning to know oneself in the most intimate thoughts

Yes I am scandalous
because I point to my truth and my nakedness as a woman,

yes I am scandalous
because I cry my sorrow and my hope
my desire, my hunger and my thirst.

to write
is to describe the multiple faces of man
the beautiful and the ugly
the tender and the cruel.

to write is to die in front of a person
upon whom you look, unmoved,

it is to drown in sight of a boat that passes close
without seeing you.

To write
is to be the boat that will save
the drowning.

To write
is to live on a cliff's edge
clinging to a blade
of grass.

3

He has begun to speak to me
with his eight small teeth,
drool on his lips.
He tells me with his eyes
things that seem to him important,
perhaps he is speaking to me of war
and the children born
to die every day,
or perhaps he is telling me
of islands far away,
of birds
of dreams
of crises
of famines.

I do not know if he wants to tell me
that the future will be sunny,
that a day will come
when people will live in peace.

He is occupied
with making his ten fingers move,
with convincing me that love is the natural fruit
of the tree of life,
and that he is happy
to have come to this world.

Then, suddenly, he has me entangled,
burrowing his head into my chest,
begging me to take him in my arms.
In that instant I understand
all that he wishes to say to me.

34

Five years after our encounter

I moved away from the noise
he followed me
he sat near me
I dared to put my head on his shoulder
I wanted to breathe his air
and retrieve the faint smell of his infancy

I took his hands in mine
they were moist and sticky
he started to count my fingers
to him I had thousands

Out of a silence disturbed
only by the chatter of his heart
and his breathing,
he asked in his trembling voice:
"are you afraid to love me?"

How could a woman like me
be afraid to love
in whom are found living
all paths
all songs
all kisses
all smiles?
I answered, "yes."

He nodded his head,
smiling,
so that all the words came tumbling around us
like feathers from a wounded bird.

Then he said,
"me, too."

THE PRAYER BOOK IS PUTTING ON FAT WITH IN MEMORIAM CARDS
John Minihan

Padraic Fiacc: Poet of the Troubles

Sometime in the summer of 1984 while working in Belfast, I was introduced to the writer Brian Keenan at the bar of the Europa Hotel. I can't remember what I was doing there, but it would certainly have had something to do with what's become known as 'the Troubles'. Brian had seen my photographs of Samuel Beckett and suggested I meet and photograph his friend, the poet Padraic Fiacc. He would arrange the meeting for the following day at The Crown Bar across from the Europa. That meeting would become eventful for the three of us.

Padraic Fiacc, who died in January 2019, aged 94 years, was to poetry what the artist Francis Bacon was to painting. Unlike Bacon, Fiacc spent most of his writing life in the literary wilderness. Poets and photographers are image makers. Great poets leave us great lines, as great photographers leave us great pictures. One of those memorable Fiacc images that I have lived with and can never forget is from his poem *More Terrorists*, published in his collection *Missa Terribilis*, Blackstaff, 1986:

> The prayer book is putting on fat
> With in memoriam cards.

1986 was the same year that Brian Keenan was kidnapped in Beirut, Lebanon and for nearly five years kept chained as a hostage, for most of that time in underground tunnels. When he was released in 1990 he published an autobiographical account called *An Evil Cradling*, winning The Irish Times Literature Prize for non-fiction in 1991.

I had always been in contact with Padraic and every time I was in Belfast I would visit. When Brian was kidnapped, I invited Padraic to London to give readings with support from actors at various Irish venues like the Mean Fiddler in Harlesden, London and literary pubs. Padraic loved being in London and was happy to support all we were doing for Brian who had done his thesis on Fiacc while at university. Over the years that Padraic visited me in London and Oxford I got to know about the man born Patrick Joseph O'Connor in Belfast in 1924. His family emigrated to the United States in 1929 settling in New York City, in an area of West Side Manhattan known as Hell's Kitchen, an area populated mainly by the Irish where violence and poverty were part of daily life. Film directors Jules Dassin made the film noir classic *The Naked City* in 1948 and William Friedkin shot *The French Connection* in 1971; true story about an Irish cop called Eddie Egan. Padraic told me he would see the camera crews on the streets daily.

Many years ago I picked up a copy of Padraic Fiacc's senior yearbook (1942) from when he was a student of Haaren High School, Brooklyn where he co-edited the literary supplement. He would talk to me about his friend, the poet Padraic Colum, who taught in New York.

Padraic loved the poems of Gerard Manley Hopkins, Baudelaire and the First World War poet Edward Thomas who wrote the poem *Adlestrop*, based on a railway journey Thomas took on 24th June 1914, during which his train stopped at the now closed station in the Gloucestershire village of Adlestrop.

When Padraic visited me in Chipping Norton, Oxfordshire in 1995, I drove him to the village of Adlestrop to take a picture of the sign which pleased him greatly. He was an enormously engaging, enriching and provocative a person as I have ever met; at times a smouldering volcano who consistently confronted the horrors of the Northern Ireland Troubles, who could not bear phoneys. He spoke and wrote the truth. He was a Christ-haunted man and a secular mystic with an acute sensitivity to the agony of life, an agony which became the predominant feature of many of his poems. He was always happy to allow me to take photographs and particularly fond of my friend, the blind poet John Heath-Stubbs, who would come to visit me in Chipping Norton, Oxfordshire and West Cork from his home in Bayswater, London. They were both mavericks. I had introduced them to each other on many occasions in London and Oxford. John liked Padraic Fiacc and thought him a fine poet. John should have been the poet laureate and Padraic Fiacc, as the poet of the Northern Irish Troubles, deserved to receive much greater recognition.

Belfast 1984

The poet Padraic Fiacc photographed in the medieval graveyard, Athy, Co. Kildare, Ireland in 1988. Padraic came to Athy to be photographed to support Brian Keenan who became a hostage in Beirut, Lebanon from 1986 to 1990. It was Brian Keenan who introduced me to the poet Padraic Fiacc in Belfast in 1984.

Col John McMillen

The Medieval Cemetery in Athy, Co. Kildare 1988

Athy, Co. Kildare 1989

The poet Padraic Rice Pictured in a Dublin Pub, 1989. © John Minihan

Dublin 1989

John Minihan Exhibition at Leicester Arts Centre 1989

London 1990 (outside Bernard Stone's Bookshop, Bloomsbury)

London 1990

Pádraic Rua is one of the few poets who confronted the Horror of the Northern Ireland 'Iron Clays' head on. A stoutly Honest voice bearing testimony to the absolute arid of violence. photographed beside the Altar Stone in Goleen, Co. Cork. Ireland 1998. (c) John Minihan

The Altar Stone, Goleen, Co. Cork 1998

the poet from Belfast, Padraic Fiacc photograph is a nursing home January 2016 (C) John Minihan

Belfast 2016

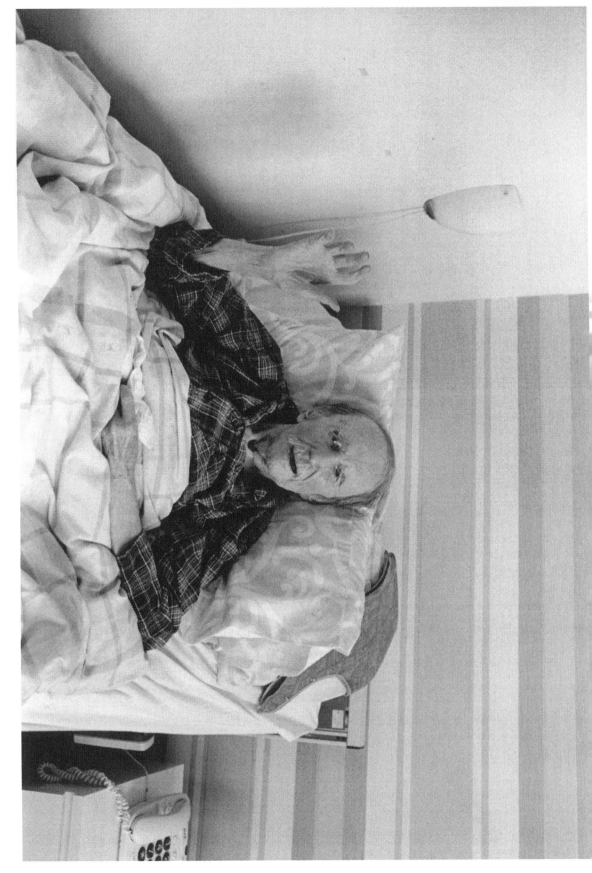

Belfast 2017

The Southword Summer Literary Essay Competition

1st & 2nd Prize:

€500

Publication in *Southword 39* (September 2020)

The competition is open to original, unpublished, personal essays between 2500–5000 words. We're looking for personal essays which border on memoir – gripping essays full of memories and feelings. The best indicator of the kind of thing which interests us is what we have published in past issues; essays by Kim Addonizio, Sandra Beasley, Simon Van Booy, Carlo Geblér, Thomas Lynch and Anthony Walton.

Essays will be judged anonymously by editor Patrick Cotter. Two essays will be chosen and published in *Southword 39*, Autumn 2020. The winning authors will each receive a prize of €500. There is an entry fee of €10.

Deadline: June 30th 2020
Guidelines: www.southword.submittable.com

THE SEÁN O'FAOLÁIN INTERNATIONAL SHORT STORY COMPETITION

1st Prize:

€2,000

1-week residency at Anam Cara Writer's & Artist's Retreat

Offered a reading and accommodation for four nights during
the Cork International Short Story Festival (September 2020)

Publication in *Southword 40* (March 2021)

2nd Prize:

€500 & publication in *Southword 40*

Four runners-up will be published in *Southword 40* and receive €250 (publication fee)

The competition is open to original, unpublished and unbroadcast short stories in the
English language of 3,000 words or fewer. The story can be on any subject, in any style,
by a writer of any nationality, living anywhere in the world. Translated work is not in the
scope of this competition.

Deadline: July 31st 2020
Guidelines: www.munsterlit.ie

THE JOHN MONTAGUE INTERNATIONAL POETRY FELLOWSHIP

The John Montague International Poetry Fellowship is an initiative of the Munster Literature Centre and is made possible through the very generous sponsorship of University College Cork. The fellowship acknowledges the special place of poetry in the cultural history and contemporary practice of Cork City.

The successful fellow will benefit from the prestige of receiving a highly competitive international literary award, which will not only allow the candidate to spend time concentrating on their own work, but also to acquire experience in literary mentoring and the teaching of writing in an academic context. The successful candidate will have the opportunity to be inspired by living in one of Europe's oldest cities, with a well-developed cultural infrastructure and a thriving literary community. The successful fellow will receive a monthly stipend of €2,000 (totalling €6,000) and self-catering accommodation. The costs of travel to and from Cork will also be covered.

The fellowship requires the poet to reside in Cork for twelve weeks in 2021 and find time to work on their own writing. The poetry fellow will arrive in late January and depart in late April. The fellow will contribute a public reading and a four-morning poetry masterclass to the Cork International Poetry Festival, the largest annual poetry festival in Ireland. During their twelve-week stay they will provide a 5-credit workshop with the creative writing department of University College Cork. Their mentoring duties will consist of devoting two hours each, per week, to two Cork poets over eight weeks (32 hours total). They will be welcomed into the literary and social life of the city where they will have the opportunity to network with resident established writers. They will present a farewell public reading at the Boole Library of University College Cork. The recipient will be a poet of international standing. Fellowship applications are invited from poets working in English from outside Ireland.

The poetry fellow must have at least two full-length collections of poetry published. The successful candidate will be a poet respected by peers and preferably have experience in the coaching or teaching of other writers through workshops and/or mentoring, inside or outside a formal academic setting.

Deadline: August 31st 2020
Guidelines: www.southword.submittable.com

FOOL FOR POETRY INTERNATIONAL
CHAPBOOK COMPETITION 2020

1st Prize: €1,000

2nd Prize: €500

Both receive chapbook publication and 25 complimentary copies

Both offered a reading and accommodation for three nights
during the Cork International Poetry Festival (March 2021)

This competition is open to new, emerging and established poets from any country. At least one of these winners will be the highest scoring manuscript entered by a debutant poet with no previously published solo collection (full-length or chapbook). Up to 25 other entrants will be publicly listed as "highly commended".

Manuscripts must be 16–24 pages in length, in the English language and the sole work of the entrant with no pastiches, translations or "versions." The poems can be in verse or prose.

There is an entrance fee of €25 for each manuscript. Entrants may enter more than one manuscript. The winners will be selected by a panel of renowned poets.

The winning chapbooks will be published by Southword Editions and launched at the Cork International Poetry Festival (March 2021). They will be for sale internationally through our own website, Amazon and selected independent booksellers.

Deadline: August 31st 2020
Guidelines: www.munsterlit.ie

CONTRIBUTORS

Mike Allen was born in London. He is working on a collection of stories.

Maram al-Masri is a Syrian poet living in France. She has published three collections in English translation: *Red Cherry on the White Floor* (Bloodaxe/Copper Caynyon), *Barefoot Souls* (Arc) and *Liberty Walks Naked* (Southword Editions). A fourth collection in English, *The Abduction*, the third to be translated by Theo Dorgan appears from Southword Editions in 2020.

Cristina Ioana Aramă is an 18-year-old high school student from Bucharest, and the founder of a monthly poetry club for teenagers.

Dean Browne's poems have appeared in *Banshee, Crannóg, Poetry Magazine, The Tangerine* and *The Well Review.* He lives in Berlin.

Chris Burke is a writer and journalist whose debut poetry collection *The Noise of Everything at Once* appeared in 2017.

Marie Coveney is a Cork painter and poet. She was published in *Dedalus Measuring,* and won The Listowel Single Poetry Prize in 2008.

Theo Dorgan's most recent books are *ORPHEUS,* (Dedalus Press) and *BAILÉID GIOFÓGACHA,* his translations into Irish of Lorca's *ROMANCERO GITANO* (Coiscéim).

Cian Ferriter lives and works in Dublin. He was winner of the 2019 Westival International Poetry Competition

Carlo Gébler lives in Enniskillen with his wife, Tyga. He teaches at Trinity, HMP Maghaberry and Hydebank Young Offenders' Centre.

Shelley Hastings lives in London. Her writing about performance has been published by *Unbound* and *This Is Tomorrow.* www.shelleyhastings.co.uk / @peckhamshell

Peter Hughes is from Monaghan Town, where he works as a journalist and editor with the *Northern Standard* provincial newspaper.

Justin Hunt is a native Kansan. A selection of his published poetry and nonfiction may be read at www.justinhunt.online.

Kelly Kirwan studied writing and literature at New York University and currently lives in Brooklyn, New York.

Kathryn Merwin is a writer based in Baltimore. Her debut chapbook, *Womanskin*, is forthcoming from CutBank Chapbooks.

John Minihan's photographs of Padraic Fiacc will be exhibited in Linen Hall Library in Belfast throughout the month of June 2020.

Theresa Muñoz won a Muriel Spark Centenary Award in 2018 to write a sequence on Spark's life, legacy and letters.

Jed Myers lives in Seattle. His recent book is *The Marriage of Space and Time*. He edits poetry for *Bracken*.

Kęstutis Navakas (1964-2020) published eight books of poetry, a novel, essay collections and translations. He won all the major literary prizes in Lithuania.

Katherine Noble is an English teacher in Austin, Texas and recent graduate of the Michener Center for Writers.

Jean Roarty, from Dublin, writes short stories. She has had stories published in anthologies by Labello Press and Magic Oxygen.

Daphne Rocou is a Greek photographer and artist living in Athens. She creates photo stories in the style of "tableaux vivants" using fictional personalities and events in order to present reality. She works with volunteers who participate in the creation of the story.

Jennifer Saunders is the author of *Self-Portrait with Housewife* (Tebot Bach, 2019). She lives in Switzerland.

Melissa Studdard is the author of the poetry collection *I Ate the Cosmos for Breakfast* and other books.

Rimas Uzgiris is the author of one poetry collection, *North of Paradise*, and translator of five. Raised in the States, he teaches at Vilnius University.

Anthony Walton is the author of *Mississippi*. His work has appeared in *The New Yorker*, *The New York Times*, and dozens of other journals.

Leslie Williams' most recent collection is *Even the Dark*.

Mary Woodward has published a pamphlet, *Almost like Talking* (Smith | Doorstop, 1993) and a collection, *The White Valentine* (Worple Press, 2013).

HOW TO SUBMIT

Southword welcomes unsolicited submissions of original work in fiction and poetry during the following open submission periods:

POETRY

What to submit:	Up to four poems in a single file
When to submit:	December 1st, 2020 – February 28th, 2021
Payment:	*Southword* will pay €40 per poem

FICTION

What to submit:	One short story (no longer than 5,000 words)
When to submit:	January 1st – March 31st, 2021
Payment:	*Southword* will pay €250 for a short story of 3,000 – 5,000 words

Submissions will be accepted through our Submittable portal online.
Visit www.southword.submittable.com for further guidelines.

Note: If you your work has been selected from an unsolicited submission and published in *Southword*, we ask that you please wait two years before submitting again.